H Martin Reekie

Analogue Circuit Design

a first course

 Chartwell-Bratt

 Studentlitteratur

British Library Cataloguing in Publication Data
Reekie, H. Martin
    Analogue circuit design
    1. Analogue circuits. Design
    I. Title
    621.3815

ISBN 0-86238-286-6

© H Martin Reekie and Chartwell-Bratt Ltd, 1991

Chartwell-Bratt (Publishing and Training) Ltd
ISBN 0-86238-286-6

Printed in Sweden,
Studentlitteratur, Lund
ISBN 91-44-34391-4

1 2 3 4 5 6 7 8 9 10 | 1995 94 93 92 91

To

Christa, Philip and Thomas

CONTENTS

Preface

Useful Books

PREFACE

This book is aimed at students taking a first course in Analogue Circuit design. It assumes some basic knowledge, for example Ohm's Law and Kirchoff's Laws though even those are given early in the text as "revision".

Unavoidably, any textbook of this kind must contain a fair amount of analysis and analytical techniques. However, it has been attempted to introduce as much *design* as possible. To that end this book contains in the last Chapter a number of "extra" questions, designated "Problems". These are greatly "open-ended" in that they usually have no unique solution; in fact there may not even be a optimum solution. Also, they often cannot be solved by using just the material available in this book. Their aim is to encourage students to use common sense, to look around them with a degree of curiosity at commonly available electrical equipment (e.g. radios, toasters, cars, hair dryers, etc) and to draw in material from other courses.

Standard tutorial questions are to be found at the end of most Chapters. In the course at Edinburgh University printed solutions to the tutorial questions are supplied as we go through the course. No printed solutions are supplied to the problems; these are the subject of discussions in the tutorials which are part of the course.

USEFUL BOOKS

1) "Electronic Devices and Circuits", T F Bogart, published by Merrill.

2) "Electronic Design: Circuits and Systems", Savant, Roden and Carpenter, published by Addison-Wesley.

3) "Analogue and Digital Electronics for Engineers", H Ahmed and P J Spreadbury, published by Cambridge University Press.

4) "Introductory Circuit Theory", J K Fidler and L. Ibbotson, published by McGraw-Hill.

5) "Introductory Circuit Analysis", R L Boylestead, published by Merrill.

Also useful are:-

6) "Integrated Electronics", Millman and Halkias, published by McGraw-Hill

7) "Microelectronics: Digital and Analog Circuits and Systems", Millman, published by McGraw-Hill

8) "Microelectronics", Millman and Gabrel, published by McGraw-Hill

Chapter 1

OBSERVATIONS ABOUT CIRCUIT DESIGN

This book is not strong on equations. Instead we will try to introduce *concepts*. In many situations in Engineering one can go a long way with ideas like "if we make the input rise slightly the output will fall a lot". This statement is the sort of thing one can say about a high gain inverting amplifier.

Unfortunately, it is sometimes required to be a little more specific and so equations will be required. However they will usually be fairly simple equations which one can re-develop as one goes along, rather than try to remember.

We will *try* to work as far as possible *designing* circuits rather than analysing circuits. This is not easy as one must be able to analyse a circuit (to check correctness) before one can design it. However, I would like to think that in this book design will be emphasised as much as possible.

In analogue work there is seldom one circuit that is the best for a certain task. Sometimes there are many standard circuits which will operate as required in which case *thought* is required to decide which is the most appropriate. Many factors will have to be taken into account in making decisions, some of which might be:-

1) The obvious - does it work?

2) Cost - *very* important.

3) Lack of circuit sensitivity to component parameters. This virtue, if present, allows us, for example, to replace dead components in the circuit with new ones without having to set-up the whole circuit again.

4)   Power dissipation.

5)   Stability of the circuit with respect to temperature and aging.

6)   Ease of interfacing with surrounding circuitry.

7)   Ease of modification if required later.

8)   In-house experience. If all the workers building and testing the circuit
     are used to do things in a certain way it will be best to try and keep to
     that method. For example, introducing MOS, static-sensitive,
     components to a workforce used to dealing exclusively with bipolar
     components will cause a headache all round. Undoubtably the worst
     headache will be reserved for the designer.

Sometimes there is no standard circuit which will work as required and we
have to design something completely novel. This not only requires thought,
it requires some intuition. Intuition is harder to teach and really comes with
experience. However, you should try to *understand* how things work, *not* just
learn up equations. Merely learning equations is the route to becoming a
very mediocre engineer.

In analogue work we are seldom very exact. Instead we tend to rely on high
gain components (how high - don't know - *fairly* high) with lots of feedback.
There is seldom a unique answer to any question; there are almost always far
more degrees of freedom than constraints.

A simple example of unique answers not being available might be- "Design a
simple potential divider to give 4.9V from a 15V supply". The circuit is
shown in Figure 1.1:-

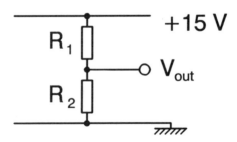

Figure 1.1: Potential Divider

Clearly we will have:— $R_2/(R_1 + R_2) * 15 = 4.9$

which can be rewritten as:— $R_1 = (4.9/10.1) * R_2$

but we do not have enough constraints to actually decide values for R_1 and R_2. We must either pick a value for one "at random" or add constraints.

Suppose we add the constraint "The output impedance of the potential divider must be exactly 2.5kΩ". Now the Thenevin equivalent of the circuit is given in Figure 1.2:-

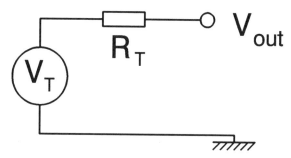

Figure 1.2: Thenevin equivalent of Potential Divider

where $R_T = R_1 \| R_2$. Note the nomenclature " $\|$ ". It means "in parallel with". In this case R_T is equal to R_1 in parallel with R_2. The potential divider output impedance is equal to R_T so

$$R_T = R_1 R_2/(R_1 + R_2) = 2.5k\Omega$$

Adding this to our previous constraint, "$R_1 = (4.9/10.1) R_2$", we obtain:-

$$R_1 = 7.6531k\Omega \quad \text{and} \quad R_2 = 3.71287k\Omega$$

We now have unique answers. However, resistors of those values are hard to find in the stores. We would have to make them up from other, more standard, values.

There are a number of ranges of standard resistor values, the simplest two of which are in the following table. Values given in **bold** font are in the simplest (cheapest) range while values given in the normal font are slightly less usual (a little bit more expensive).

STANDARD RESISTOR VALUES											
10	**12**	**15**	**18**	**22**	**27**	**33**	**39**	**47**	**56**	**68**	**82**
11	13	16	20	24	30	36	43	51	62	75	91

The above values are given in ohms but multiples of ten of the above in the range 10Ω to $1M\Omega$ are also standard. Thus a $1k\Omega$ resistor is absolutely "bog-standard", while a $240k\Omega$ resistor, though quite possible, is going to take a little bit more finding.

You should probably have the simplest range of resistor values somewhere in your mind. It makes life a lot easier when doing real designs!

To return to our example. We need $R_2 = 3.71287k\Omega$. We could make this up using two series connected $3.6k\Omega$ and 110Ω resistors. The R_1 resistor ($7.6531k\Omega$) could be a $7.5k\Omega$ resistor in series with 150Ω. Three of these resistors are in the less simple range while one is in the simplest range. In volume such resistors cost about 2p each so the total cost would be 8p.

The last sentence of the previous paragraph gives a hint to another constraint we could apply. Cost. Perhaps we do not need an output impedance of *exactly* $2.5k\Omega$. Perhaps an output impedance of a little *less* than this would be adequate. However, we can't go a *lot* less because if we alter the circuit to give a very low output impedance the resistors will become very low in value and the power dissipated in the potential divider will increase unacceptably.

We now come to "intelligent guessing". We look at the standard resistor values which are a bit *less* than the accurate values for R_1 and R_2 and try to pair them up to give 4.9V output. Let's choose values for R_1. Pick $7.5k\Omega$. This would give $R_2 = 3.63k\Omega$, not a standard value. Try one step less in the table so $R_1 = 6.8k\Omega$. This gives $R_2 = 3.3k\Omega$ which *is* a standard value. The output impedance ($6.8k\Omega \parallel 3.3k\Omega$) is $2.2k\Omega$ which is a bit less than the required $2.5k\Omega$, but not much. The cost of the divider will now be 4p and the components will be in the stores (simplest range).

This simple example ought to demonstrate four important points:-

1)   In circuit design unique answers seldom occur.

2)   If you want unique answers you must add constraints which must often be chosen by you, the designer, rather than defined by circuit performance.

3)   A *very* important constraint is COST which must be minimised.

4)   Another important constraint which is often forgotten by novice designers is *power consumption*.

Chapter 2

REVISION

2.1 VOLTAGE

Voltage is "electromotive force" or, perhaps, electrical "pressure". It is always measured with respect to something. A point in a circuit cannot just be said to be at 4 volts. It must be at 4V with respect to something. Sometimes we apply a kind of short-hand and assume that all voltages are with respect to ground *but we must remember that this assumption is being made.*

Remember that voltages have signs attached. Therefore we can say that if the voltage from point A to point B is 6V, then the voltage from point B to point A is −6V.

2.2 CURRENT

Current is a measure of flow, in this case the flow of charge. Normally electrons carry the charge and they are the ones that move around so current usually flows from negative to positive. That is what you were told in school. *But that is not the way conventional current flow is defined.* We *always* define current flow *from positive to negative.* The whole thing is just a matter of definition anyway; way back in history the charge on an electron could have been defined as positive and physics would have got along just fine.

Remember:- Current flows from positive to negative.

This all implies that *current is a signed quantity.* A current of I_E flowing *into* a transistor is *exactly* the same as a current of $-I_E$ flowing *out* of a transistor.

When analysing circuits we very often use this idea of drawing an arrow in an arbitrary direction and stating that the current flowing this way is "I". Once

the analysis is complete we may find that the numerical value for "I" is
negative. OK, that's fine, it just means that a current of "+I" is flowing the
other way, against the arrow we drew.

2.3 OHM'S LAW   V = IR

If we have a constant resistance and increase the voltage (pressure) across it,
extra current flows. If voltage is constant and we decrease the resistance,
more current flows.

Ohm's Law is possibly the most basic concept in circuit design. *It is never
suspended*! This last observation always holds true, even when considering
"nasty" things like current sources. For example, a real current source
working from a 5V power supply, rated at 1A and connected to a 1MΩ
resistor will simply fail to work. One Amp through 1MΩ implies that 1MV
is available. In fact there is only a 5V power supply available so the current
source will simply fail to drive the rated current. Ohm's Law *always* works!

2.4 POWER EQUATIONS

Power = Volts * Amps

This is a very basic equation and should not be forgotten. It often arises
when specifying a design. For example "Design a widget which works from a
15V power supply and consumes 30mW". Clearly the widget will draw 2mA.

Power = Volts^2/Resistance   and   Power = Current^2 * Resistance

These relate Current, Voltage and Resistance but are just combinations of
Ohm's Law and P=VI. They tell you the power dissipated in individual
resistors but are no good at, for example, telling us the power dissipated in
transistors (what's the resistance of a transistor?).

Please note that transistors DO dissipate power! Try overdriving one and then
touch it. That sizzling sound is your skin coming off! Transistors are *said* to
dissipate no power if they are full OFF (true) or full ON (nearly true). In
analogue circuit design we almost always have transistors *half ON*.

Compare transistors with light switches. A light switch, whether ON or OFF,
does not normally get hot so it dissipates no power. Now try carefully

turning the light switch *half* ON. You'll know you have succeeded when you hear the fizzing. Do you smell the burning? That's power being dissipated. Do it in your house, not in the University.

2.5 KIRCHOFF'S VOLTAGE LAW

Kirchoff's voltage law states that the sum of voltages around a loop is zero. Another way of looking at this is to say that if two systems or circuits or components are connected in parallel the voltage across them is equal. Consider the diagram given in Figure 2.1.

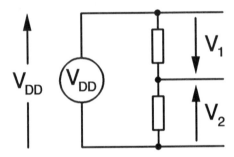

Figure 2.1: Simple Circuit Illustrating a Voltage Loop

Here we see a little circuit with voltages defined oddly; voltage V_2 is defined "backwards" when compared to the "natural" way of doing things. Kirchoff's voltage laws state that the sum of voltages round the loop *in one direction* is zero. Hence, in the diagram, $V_{DD} + V_1 - V_2 = 0$. Note that we have had to say $-V_2$ because V_2 is defined in the diagram "backwards". We can define any voltage in any part of any circuit to be in either direction. We may then use this definition in a circuit analysis and so discover that the voltage is negative. This is *identical* to a equal, positive, voltage defined the other way.

2.6 KIRCHOFF'S CURRENT LAW

Kirchoff's current law states that the sum of currents into a node (or system) must be zero. Now, assuming that there *are* some currents flowing, this implies that some of the currents must be negative.

2.7 THEVENIN'S THEOREM

Any one-port network composed entirely of *sources* and linear *resistances* is equivalent to a voltage source V_T in series with a resistor R_T. This is shown in Figure 2.2.

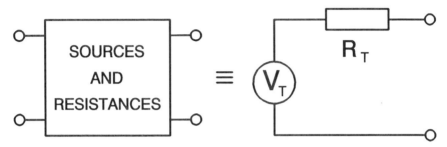

Figure 2.2: Thenevin Equivalence

To find the value of V_T, draw no current from the output and measure the voltage. That's V_T. (No current drawn implies no current in R_T which implies no drop across it.)

To find the value of R_T try one of the following methods:-

1) Short circuit the output with an ammeter. Measure the current, I. V_T is driving a current I through R_T. Therefore $R_T = V_T/I$.

2) Set $V_T = 0$ (*which makes it into a short circuit*) and measure the resistance R_T with an ohmmeter.

2.8 NORTON'S THEOREM

Any one-port network composed entirely of *sources* and linear *resistances* is equivalent to a current source I_N in parallel with a resistor R_N. This is shown in Figure 2.3.

To find the value of I_N, short circuit the output with an ammeter and measure the current which will be I_N.

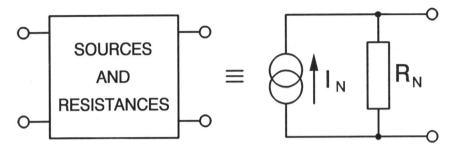

Figure 2.3: Norton Equivalence

To find the value of R_N try one of the following methods:-

1) Draw no current from the output and measure the voltage, V. The current I_N is causing a voltage, V, across R_N. Therefore $R_N = V/I_N$.

2) Set $I_N = 0$ (*which makes it into an open circuit*) and measure the resistance R_N with an ohmmeter.

2.9 SUPERPOSITION

If cause and effect are *linearly* related, the total effect of several causes acting simultaneously is equal to the sum of the effects of the individual causes acting one at a time.

In other words, to determine the response of a linear circuit to a collection of sources, determine the response to each *independent* source, one at a time, assuming that all other *independent* sources are zero. Sum the results to get the total response.

Note that when a voltage source is set to zero it becomes a *short circuit* (there are zero volts across a short circuit). When a current source is set to zero it becomes an *open circuit* (there is no current through an open circuit).

2.10 MAXIMUM POWER TRANSFER

This is not one we will use much in this book but it is important all the same. Figure 2.4 shows a voltage source, V_S, of internal impedance R_S driving a load of value R_L.

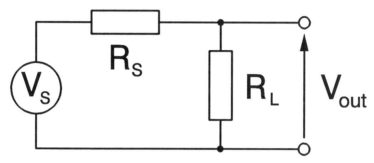

Figure 2.4: Power from Source to Load

The power dissipated in R_L, P_{out}, is given by:-

$$P_{out} = \frac{V_{out}^2}{R_L} = \frac{R_2}{(R_1 + R_2)^2} V_s^2$$

A little calculus shows that the maximum output power occurs when $R_L = R_S$.

Note that this is for maximum *power* transfer. This rule does *not* apply for maximum voltage or current transfer.

To transfer maximum *voltage* (the usual requirement in the circuits shown in this book) R_S should be *low* and R_L should be *high*.

To transfer maximum *current* R_L should be *low*.

QUESTIONS

2.1) Calculate the currents in the three branches of each of the circuits in Figure 2.5.

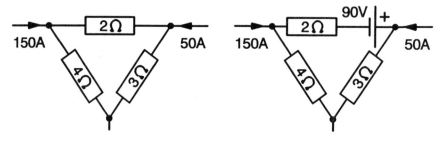

Figure 2.5

2.2) For the circuit in Figure 2.6, calculate the current in the 10Ω resistor using Kirchoff's law(s).

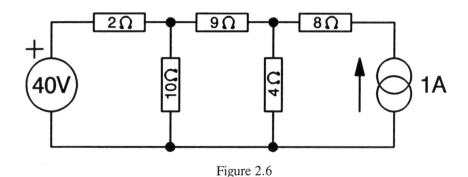

Figure 2.6

2.3) In figure 2.7 a load of 6Ω is supplied by a parallel combination of two batteries. Battery A has an open circuit voltage of 42V and an internal resistance of 12Ω; battery B has an open circuit voltage of 35V and an internal resistance of 3Ω. Determine the current I supplied by battery B and calculate the power dissipated internally by battery B. Use (a) the theory of superposition and (b) Thevenin's theorem.

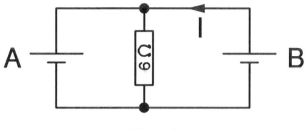

Figure 2.7

2.4) For the circuit of Figure 2.8, calculate the current in the 10Ω resistor using Kirchoff's law(s). Find also the voltage across the 4Ω resistor.

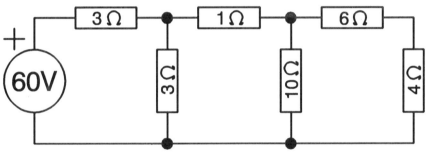

Figure 2.8

2.5) Shown in Figure 2.9 is a simple transistor circuit.

What are the voltages V_E and V_S with respect to ground? Are V_{out} and V_R positive or negative? Given that I_B is small and positive, are I_C and I_E positive or negative? Which of I_C and I_E is larger in magnitude?

2.6) Shown in Figure 2.10(a) is a simple heater with a variable heat output. The resistor is a long coil of resistance wire and the effective length (and so resistance) of the wire is adjusted by a "wiper", the position of which is variable. If the supply voltage is constant and I wish to increase the heat output do I move the wiper towards end "A" or "B"?

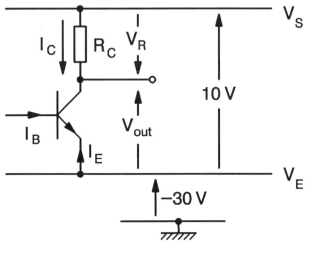

Figure 2.9

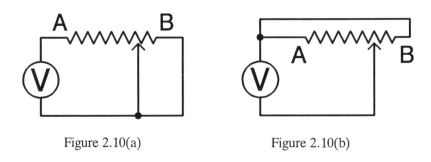

Figure 2.10(a)   Figure 2.10(b)

Suppose, now, that we modify the circuit to be that shown in Figure 2.10(b). Sketch a graph showing the variation of heat output against wiper position.

Suppose the horrible electric bar fire you have at home blew its element. Since the break was near the end and the fire was so old there was no chance of getting a new element you decided to unwind the element a bit and stretch the wire to the end contact. Would the fire be hotter or colder? Any comment on the life expectancy of the "new" element?

2.7) Shown in Figure 2.11 is a Wheatstone Bridge.

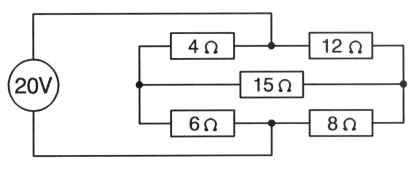

Figure 2.11

Find the current in the 15Ω resistor. [Hint:- This is a *lot* easier if you can use Thenevin's theorem.] Hence find the current in the 4Ω resistor.

2.8) Shown in Figure 2.12 is a collection of resistors, current sources and voltage sources.

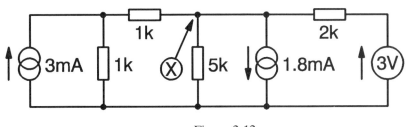

Figure 2.12

Using Norton's and Thenevin's theorems where appropriate, find the voltage on point X. Hence, find the current in the horizontal 1kΩ resistor. [Note:- This is requires only mental arithmetic and sketches]

2.9) Using the principle of superposition, find the current in the 12kΩ resistor in Figure 2.13.

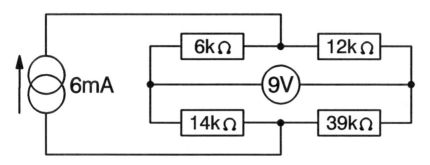

Figure 2.13

Chapter 3

DIODE MODELS

A diode is usually made from the junction between a piece of n-type semiconductor and a piece of p-type semiconductor. †

Conventional current in a conventional diode is normally thought of as flowing from the p-type to the n-type semiconductor. However, if we reverse bias the diode (+ve voltage on the n-type, −ve voltage on the p-type) a *small* current will flow. This current, often labelled I_s, is the *reverse saturation current*. For a normal discrete diode I_s might be in the very low μA range. For a small diode on an integrated circuit I_s is in the order of 10^{-13}A.

When we forward bias the diode so that sizable amounts of current flow we will find a voltage of about 0.7V across the diode. This is called the *diode forward voltage*.

The standard equation describing the flow of current through a diode is:-

$$I = I_s[\exp(qV/mkT) - 1]$$

where:- I is the diode current
V is the voltage across the diode
I_s is the reverse saturation current
q is electron charge $(1.6 * 10^{-19}$ Coulombs)
k is the Boltzmann constant $(1.38 * 10^{-23}$ J$K^{-1})$
T is temperature in degrees Kelvin and
m is the fudge factor required to make the whole thing work.

---

† Diodes can actually occur between a great many materials, for example corrosion products and metals in TV antennae, but the main exception we will meet to this statement, when considering electronic circuits, is the Schottky diode which occurs between a lightly doped n-type semiconductor and a metal.

"m" is between 1 and 2, normally closer to 2. m=1 for high current silicon diodes and m=2 for low current silicon diodes and all germanium diodes. We will always be looking at low current silicon diodes so we will take m=2.

At room temperature and with m=2 we get mkT/q $\approx$ 52mV.

Note that this diode equation is a *model* which allows us to describe the operation of a real diode mathematically. As with all models, it is an *approximation* to reality. Even if we adjust the value of "m" we will still only have an approximation to the voltage/current relationship of any particular diode. However, in this case the approximation is actually fairly good *if* we have the right parameters to plug into the equation. This last point is particularly important because I_s varies with processing and I_s and, of course, T varies dramatically with temperature.

You will see that if we plug V=0 into the diode equation we get I=0 This is nice because it ought to work like that. However, we are often rather lazy when using this diode equation and simplify it to become:-

$$I = I_s [\exp(qV/mkT)]$$

You will see that the "−1" has disappeared. The resulting equation describes reasonably well what happens when the diode is conducting forwards but is less good when the voltage across the diode is small (< 0.7V?) or negative.

Shown in Figure 3.1 is the voltage/current graph for a diode.

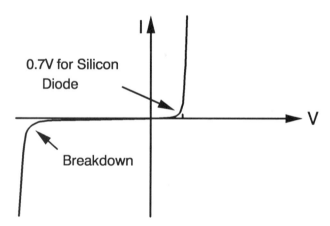

Figure 3.1: Diode voltage/current graph

As you can see, the graph does not show zero current for voltages of less than 0.7V. The diode forward voltage is about 0.7V *if sizable currents are flowing*. If the current through the diode is actually very small as is the case, for example, when it is the base/emitter junction of a transistor, the forward voltage can be significantly less, about 0.55 or 0.6V. However, this is just an added complication and normally we will use 0.7V as the standard value for the diode forward voltage.

As stated earlier, the above "accurate" diode equation is a mathematical model, albeit a fairly good one if one has the input parameters available. Other models are frequently used in an effort to cut down on the amount of computation involved.

Some of the main diode models are discussed in the following sections.

3.1 IDEAL DIODE

Here we consider the diode to be a perfect device which is a short circuit to current flowing in the forward direction and an open circuit to current flowing in the reverse direction. It has no reverse current and no forward voltage drop. This model is a bit primitive but has the merit of simplicity. It is shown in Figure 3.2(a).

3.2 IDEAL DIODE WITH THRESHOLD VOLTAGE

This models the diode as a perfect device but with a constant diode forward voltage, usually of 0.7V. There is still no reverse current but if forward current flows there is exactly 0.7V across the device. This is a very popular model and we will attempt to use it as often as possible. It is shown in Figure 3.2(b). Note that current *can* be forced through a 0.7V voltage source the "wrong" way!

3.3 IDEAL DIODE WITH THRESHOLD VOLTAGE
AND FORWARD RESISTANCE

There is still no reverse current but there is a 0.7V drop across the diode when current is *just about to flow*. At forward voltages of greater than 0.7V the diode is modelled by a resistor. This model is shown in Figure 3.2(c).

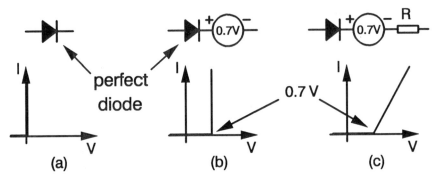

Figure 3.2: Three diode models

QUESTION

3.1) We have a mains operated power supply which generates +10V and also a 9V battery. A circuit which requires at least 8V is to be kept in continuous operation, even in the event of mains failure. Design an appropriate switching circuit.

Chapter 4

BIPOLAR JUNCTION TRANSISTOR

The bipolar transistor is a three-terminal device. It is a sandwich of either p-type, n-type, p-type semiconductor (a PNP device) or n-type, p-type, n-type semiconductor (an NPN device). The middle layer of the sandwich is the BASE and the outer two layers are the COLLECTOR and the EMITTER. The device is NOT symmetrical so it *does* matter which end is the collector and which is the emitter but we'll come to that later.

The symbols and the very approximate construction of a PNP and an NPN transistor are given in Figure 4.1.

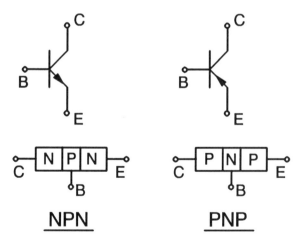

Figure 4.1: A PNP and an NPN Transistor Symbol and Approximate Construction

4.1 TRANSISTOR OPERATION

Let's start with a PNP transistor connected as shown in Figure 4.2

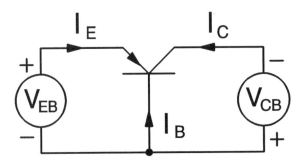

Figure 4.2: PNP Transistor connected Common Base

This is connected in the Common Base configuration because there are two current loops, one through the battery V_{EB} and one through the battery V_{CB} and the base connection is common to them both.

Let's start by looking at a hole sitting in the emitter region of the transistor. The emitter region is p-type so a hole in there is a *majority* current carrier. This hole cannot "see" the collector because it is shielded from it by the base. However the base is negative with respect to the emitter (or the emitter is positive with respect to the base which is the same thing) so the hole will think that it is a good idea to nip across to the base. Off it goes. Once it arrives in the base region it is a hole in an area of n-type semiconductor and so it is a *minority* charge carrier. Two things might happen:-

1) If might be "eaten up" by a nearby electron. This recombination of an electron and a hole will cause current to flow in the base connection. If the base region is fairly thick this is almost certain to happen.

2) If the base region is rather thin there is another possibility. The hole, in the base region, will now "see" the collector and the collector, being very negative, is a very desirable place for a hole to go. Off it goes again, this time at speed. If it is lucky it might avoid the electrons, and so avoid recombination and get into the collector, where it is safe because there it is a majority charge carrier.

Let us suppose that the base region is *very* thin. Transistor manufacturers go to great lengths to ensure that this is the case so it is a reasonable assumption. Then we can hope that most holes leaving the emitter will make it to the collector.

Now Kirchoff's current laws say that $I_C + I_B + I_E = 0$, assuming that the current directions are as defined in Figure 4.2, i.e. all *in* to the transistor. Actually, considering conventional current flow, only I_E is going in to the transistor and the other two are leaving. Thus, returning to the definitions of Figure 4.2, I_B and I_C are negative and I_E is positive. (Note that this will be exactly reversed for an NPN transistor.)

We now define a variable, α, such that:- $\alpha = -I_C/I_E$.

Because $I_E = -(I_C + I_B)$, $\alpha < 1$. Since part of this transistor game is to get I_B to be as small as possible, I_E and I_C will be very nearly equal (in magnitude) so α should be very near to one. Typically

$$0.9 < \alpha < 0.998$$

There is another related definition which is the one more often used. This is for β which is defined as:-

$$\beta = I_C/I_B$$

As I_B is normally small, β should be large. Typically it is in the range:-

$$10 < \beta < 500$$

with higher β implying a better transistor (at least in terms of gain).

A combination of these two definitions gives:-

$$\alpha = \frac{\beta}{(1 + \beta)} \quad \text{and} \quad \beta = \frac{\alpha}{(1 - \alpha)}$$

The parameter β is critical to transistor design in this course. It is almost exactly equal to the parameter h_{fe}, used in the so-called h-parameter model of a transistor, though it is defined slightly differently. In this course we will say $\beta = h_{fe}$. The most important transistor design equation in this course is:-

$$I_C = \beta I_B$$

4.2 TRANSISTOR FABRICATION - ROUGHLY!

The emitter/base junction is just a diode so current can be carried in two ways. There will be holes going from the emitter to the collector (and we have seen what happens to them) and there will be electrons going from the base to the emitter. This latter form of current flow is not what we want for transistor action so we build the transistor in such a way that it doesn't happen much.

To avoid current flow from the base to the emitter we ensure that there are not many current carriers in the base region. We want hole current so we also ensure that there are lots of holes present in the emitter region. The way we get this desirable state of affairs is to dope the emitter region fairly heavily p-type (so-called P^+) and dope the base region only lightly (so-called N^-).

The collector region has to be fairly lightly doped so its dopant does not creep into the very thin, lightly doped base and eliminate it. However, because it has to carry serious current it needs to be heavily doped so that it has a low resistance. The compromise is to give the collector region a medium to light doping near the base and a heavy doping away from the base. It also has to collect all the current carriers sprayed out from the emitter so it should be large.

A typical "planar" transistor, drawn in cross-section, is shown in Figure 4.3.

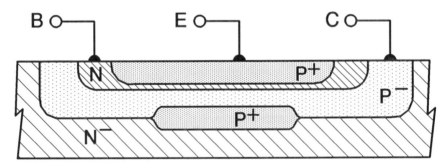

Figure 4.3: Cross-section of planar PNP Transistor (not to scale)

4.3 REGIONS OF TRANSISTOR OPERATION

Transistor characteristics can be divided into four regions:-

1) **The Cutoff Region**

Here there is no base current because the base emitter voltage is too low to allow current to flow. Hence $I_B = I_C = I_E = 0$. The base/emitter and base/collector junctions are both reverse biased (or, more accurately, they are not forward biased because they do not have 0.7 forward volts across them).

2) **The Active Region**

Nearly all analogue work is carried out in this region. In this region $I_C = \beta I_B$. The base/emitter junction is forward biased and the base/collector junction is reverse biased. For us this is the normal operating region. Note that in this region the transistor is drawing significant collector current and it has significant voltages across it. It is therefore dissipating significant power.

3) **The Saturated Region**

In a saturated transistor $I_C < \beta I_B$ *because it is limited by external circuitry.*

The transistor is ON so $V_{BE} > 0.7$ and the base/emitter junction is forward biased.

The transistor is trying its very best to let as much current as possible through so its collector/emitter "resistance" is very low. Thus V_{CE} is very low (usually between 0.2 and 0.4V). Thus the voltage from the base to the collector, V_{BC}, is positive, though not usually by more than 0.5V.

In saturation the base/emitter and base/collector junctions are both forward biased.

In terms of the arm-waving explanation of transistor operation, the current carriers from the emitter get into the base and then don't find the collector voltage very attractive (because its voltage is not very high). They then mess about in the base so long that they recombine with the majority carriers there and become base current.

For example, suppose $\beta = 100$ and $I_B = 1mA$. The transistor works from a 5V power supply and there is a 1MΩ resistor in the collector lead. By our friendly equation $I_C = \beta I_B$ we should have $I_C = 100mA$. But 100mA in the 1mΩ resistor would need 100kV! We don't have that so I_C is not 100mA. The transistor does its best to get as much current through its collector as possible but can't pull 100mA. All the current carriers from the emitter that possibly can are piling into the collector. The result in voltage terms is that the collector to emitter voltage falls to a low value called the *saturation voltage* and often written as $V_{CE(sat)}$. Typically $V_{CE(sat)}$ is in the range 0.2 to 0.4 volts. In this course we'll split the difference and go for $V_{CE(sat)} = 0.3V$.

4)   **The Reverse Region**

We don't usually want to be here! It means we have got the collector and emitter confused and are running the transistor backwards. Normally, for good transistor operation, the emitter should be heavily doped and the collector should be larger and lightly doped. If we run the thing backwards this desirable situation is reversed and, though it does work, it does not work very well (low β, among other things). Transistors are run in this region in TTL logic gates but there are special cunning reasons for this and we will not normally be concerned with this mode of operation.

There is another region of operation called, perhaps, the meltdown region. This is due to excessive power dissipation but that is another story.

4.4 COMMON BASE CONFIGURATION

Let's work with NPN transistors from now on. They are more often used because the majority current carriers are electrons which have a higher mobility than holes so NPN transistors tend to be faster. Also they usually work with positive voltages and power supplies which are nicer to work with. However, PNP transistors cannot be discarded and are very important. They work in just the same way as NPN devices except that all the power supply voltages are inverted ($-$ve becomes $+$ve and vice versa) and currents flow the opposite direction.

An NPN transistor working in common base configuration is shown in Figure 4.4.

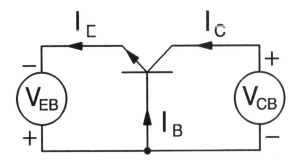

Figure 4.4: NPN transistor in Common Base Configuration

It has the current/voltage characteristics shown in Figure 4.5.

To make the circuit of Figure 4.4 produce the graphs of Figure 4.5 we first decided on a value for I_E, say 5mA. We then started V_{CB} at -0.4V and adjusted V_{EB} to get $I_E = 5$mA. We then noted I_C. We incremented V_{CB} by a bit, adjusted V_{EB} to keep I_E at 5mA and noted the new value for I_C. We kept up this process until we had covered the desired range for V_{CB}.

Another member of the family of graphs shown in Figure 4.5 was obtained by picking another value for I_E.

This family of graphs shows the three main regions of transistor operation. The section of the graphs below $V_{CB} = 0.7$V is the saturation region. In this region I_C is much less than I_E so, to make up the difference, I_B is high. Though not shown, the collector-emitter voltage is very low in this region.

The section of the graphs above $V_{CB} = 0.7$V (collector/base junction reverse biased) is the active region. Here you can see that $I_E \approx I_C$. The very small difference is the very small base current. In this region the collector-emitter voltages are high.

The cutoff region is also shown. It is the line at the bottom of the graph labeled $I_E = 0$.

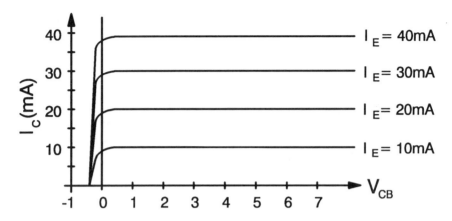

Figure 4.5: NPN Common Base Current/Voltage Characteristics

4.5 COMMON EMITTER CONFIGURATION

This is the way we will usually connect up transistors and it is shown (in principle) in Figure 4.6.

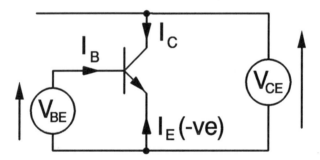

Figure 4.6: NPN Transistor in Common Emitter Configuration

Here you can see two external current paths which have the emitter lead in common. Hence Common-Emitter. Figure 4.7 shows a family of current/voltage characteristics.

These look rather different from the common-base characteristics mainly because they are graphing different quantities!

Here each member of the family of graphs corresponds to a different value of I_B. I_B is held constant and V_{CE} is swept across a range while the collector current, I_C is plotted.

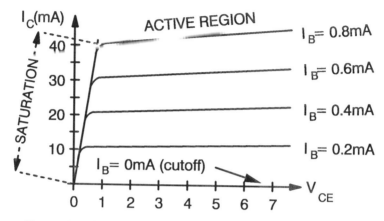

Figure 4.7: Common Emitter Current/Voltage Characteristics

Again we can see each of the three regions of operation. Cutoff is the bottom graph with $I_B = 0$. The saturation region is the left hand part of the graph where the collector voltage is very low. The active region is the rest.

Note that the graphs in the active region are not horizontal. By the equation $I_C = \beta I_B$ they should be flat because if I_B is held constant and the transistor is in the active region I_C should be constant regardless of the value of V_{CE}.

Suppose that when we performed the experiment required to produce the family of graphs in Figure 4.7 we held I_B constant by holding V_{BE} constant. Therefore a constant number of charge carriers are being injected from the emitter into the base. On arrival in the base these charge carriers want to go to the collector because the collector is at a nice high voltage. In fact, the higher the voltage on the collector the more these charge carriers want to go there. The more charge carriers that get to the collector the less there are available to become base current.

By this argument base current reduces as collector voltage rises. If we hold base current artificially constant (with a current source) this is rather like forcing more base current than the transistor needs. Therefore collector current rises with increasing collector voltage.

Whether you like this argument or not (!) this is known as the Early Effect. If we extrapolate the near horizontal sections of the family of graphs in Figure 4.7 back to negative V_{CE} voltages we will find that they all meet on the x-axis at the same value of V_{CE}. (Figure 4.8).

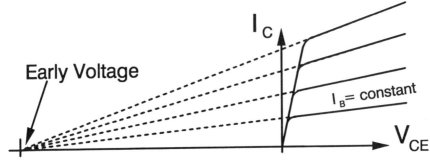

Figure 4.8: The reverse Early Voltage

This value of V_{CE} is called the *reverse Early voltage* because it was discovered by J M Early who just had a name guaranteed to confuse students of later generations. It is nothing to do with "early" as in "not late"! We never attempt to run transistors with V_{CE} equal to this Early voltage; it is just used to give a single parameter that "measures" the slope of the supposedly flat sections of the graphs.

4.6 COMMON COLLECTOR CONFIGURATION

A quite sensible common collector circuit is shown in Figure 4.9 with its characteristics shown in Figure 4.10.

It is possible to redefine the voltages on this circuit so that we see two current paths which have the collector lead in common. However it is unhelpful to do so. Instead, let's find another way of discovering which configuration a transistor is in.

The basic rule is this. Look àt the circuit to see which terminals are connected to input and output. The transistor is configured in common-(the other one) mode.

For example, in the circuit of Figure 4.9, the input is on the base and the output comes from the emitter. Therefore the transistor is working in

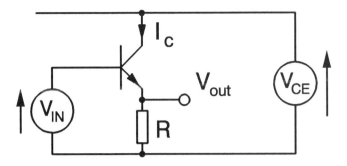

Figure 4.9: Common Collector Configuration

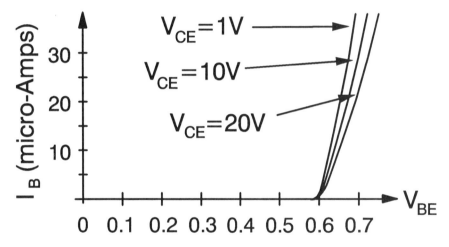

Figure 4.10: NPN Transistor Common Collector Characteristics (Base)

common-collector configuration.

Just to confuse things further, the particular circuit shown in Figure 4.9 is almost always known as an *emitter follower*. It is almost the only way the common-collector configuration is used.

It is quite possible to have a transistor configured so that it has inputs and outputs on every terminal. Then there is no way of saying what sort of configuration we have.

From the characteristics of Figure 4.10 we can see that the graphs of I_B against V_{BE} vary depending on collector voltage. The Early effect strikes again.

This circuit is a buffer amplifier with a gain of one. Notice that the input and output are separated by a single diode (the base emitter junction). Therefore there will be an approximately constant 0.7V between the input and output. If the input rises by, say, 30mV the output must rise by about 30mV. Therefore the AC gain will be about 1. We will deal with this circuit properly later.

Chapter 5

TRANSISTOR DC BIASING

Before we attempt to set up a transistor to amplify AC signals *we must set its DC operating point*. This is an absolutely *vital* concept. We *must* get the transistor operating in a correct DC fashion *before* we try to input AC signals.

For example, suppose we have in mind a transistor amplifier circuit in which the AC output signal depends on variations in collector current. If, before we input a signal, there is no collector current then it is going to be hard to get plus and minus variations in the collector current. Also, it is going to be tough to get a nice output signal if the DC conditions are so wrong that the transistor melts in the first micro-second after switch on!

Getting a nice output signal will also be difficult if the transistor is biased so that it is so hard ON that it is saturated with its collector-emitter voltage stuck at about 0.3V.

In analogue work we require transistors to be constrained to work in the active region. Only in this region do transistors work in a (something like) linear fashion.

To establish an operating point in the region it is necessary to provide appropriate DC potentials and currents using external sources.

Once a quiescent operating point is established time varying excursions of the input signal (in other words an AC input signal) should cause an output signal with the same (or same but inverted) waveform. If the output signal is not a faithful reproduction of the input signal the operating point is unsatisfactory and should be moved.

A transistor has its DC operating point constrained by three major factors (apart from having input voltages of the correct polarity!).

1)   Maximum voltages, usually $V_{CE(max)}$.

2)   Maximum currents, usually $I_{C(max)}$

3)   Maximum power dissipation, $P_{(max)}$, the one usually forgotten by students

These constraints are shown in Figure 5.1.

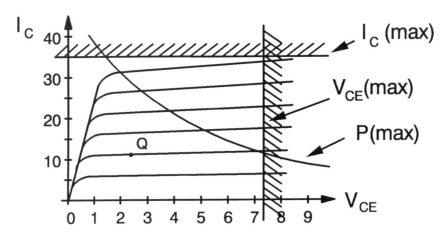

Figure 5.1: Constraints on Transistor Quiescent Point

The DC operating point, the quiescent point, must be within the safe operating region. And not just on the edge either!

There are at least three simple biasing techniques and they will be examined separately in the next sections.

5.1 COMMON EMITTER FIXED BIAS

A circuit for a transistor amplifier working with this form of bias is shown in Figure 5.2.

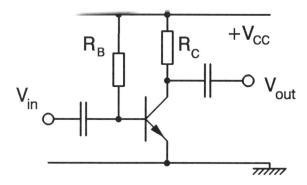

Figure 5.2: Transistor Amplifier with Fixed Bias

Here we have a resistor, R_B, providing a DC supply of base current. When we try to set up this circuit *we first completely ignore any AC signals and open circuit any capacitors*. Now suppose the collector resistor is 2kΩ and the power supply is 12V. Let us further suppose we have the family of characteristics of the transistor. We can superimpose on this family of graphs the load line. The result will be as in Figure 5.3.

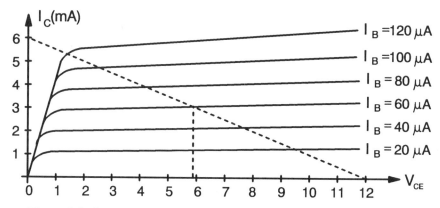

Figure 5.3: Common Emitter Transistor Characteristics with Load Line

Suppose we wish to bias the transistor so that its output voltage swing is maximised.

What is the maximum output voltage? This occurs when the transistor is OFF and so there is no current through R_C. $V_{out(max)} = 12V$.

What is the minimum output voltage? This occurs when the transistor starts to move into the saturated region. At that point $V_{CE} = V_{CE(sat)} \approx 0.3V$. Thus $V_{out(min)} = 0.3V$.

We should bias the transistor in such a way that when there is no AC input signal the output voltage is midway between its minimum and maximum voltages. In this case $V_{(out,quiescent)} = (12 + 0.3)/2 = 5.85V$.

We now drawn a line on the graph of Figure 5.3 at $V_{CE} = 5.85V$ and see where it intersects the load line. Now check to see whether we are well inside the safe operating region. If not, the collector resistor is too low or the power supply voltage is too high. Let's suppose all is well so far.

By interpolating, if necessary, between members of the family of transistors characteristics we can find the appropriate value of I_B which will set the quiescent point we need. In this case about $57\mu A$ would be about right.

Now to find the value of R_B. The voltage on the base is about 0.7V (because the base-emitter junction is a diode which is conducting forward). It might be a little less than this because $57\mu A$ is not much forward current but 0.7V will do. Then the voltage across R_B is $(12 - 0.7)V = 11.3V$ and the current through it is $57\mu A$. Therefore $R_B = 198.24k\Omega \approx 200k\Omega$. Note that we round to the nearest standard resistor value.

We could have carried out this design work without the graphs if we knew the value of β for the transistor.

Calculate the quiescent operating point as before, giving $V_{out(quiescent)} = 5.85V$. Then the voltage across R_C would be $(12 - 5.85) = 6.15V$. Because R_C is $2k\Omega$ we have $I_C = 3.075mA$. Suppose β is 50. Then $I_B = I_C/\beta = 61.5\mu A$. We now calculate R_B as before.

We now have the transistor correctly DC biased. If we now apply an AC signal to the base through a capacitor it will cause variations in base current. These, in turn, will cause variations in collector current which will cause changes in output voltage and we will have an amplifier.

The important point to note is that to complete the design of this circuit we needed the value of β. If we used the graphs we were still using β which is implicit in the graphs.

The value of β for a given type of transistor can *easily* vary by -50% to $+100\%$ of the typical value. It also varies a great deal with temperature and varies slightly with aging. Therefore this circuit meets hardly any of the needs of a good analogue design.

THIS IS NOT A VERY GOOD WAY TO BIAS A TRANSISTOR IN PRACTICE!!

5.2 COMMON EMITTER DC BIAS with EMITTER RESISTOR

Shown in Figure 5.4 is a common emitter amplifier with an emitter resistor, R_E.

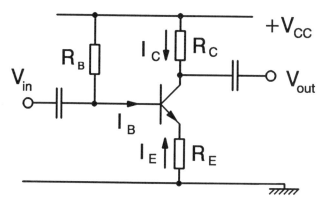

Figure 5.4: Common Emitter Amplifier with an Emitter Resistor

Unfortunately it is time to do a little analysis. Recall that $I_C + I_E + I_B = 0$ with I_C, I_E and I_B directions defined *into* the transistor as shown in Figure 5.4. Also $I_C = \beta I_B$. These two together give:-

$$I_E = -(\beta + 1) I_B$$

Now the power supply voltage is equal to the voltage across R_B plus 0.7V plus the voltage across R_E. Therefore:-

$$V_{CC} = I_B R_B + 0.7 + (1 + \beta) I_B R_E$$

This can be turned around give:- $\quad I_B = \dfrac{V_{CC} - 0.7}{R_B + (1 + \beta) R_E}$

Note the term $(1 + \beta) R_E$ term in the denominator. Because of it there is a *tendency* for I_B to fall as β rises. This *tends* to cancel the rise in I_C which happens when β rises.

We can show this tendency by continuing the equations. From the above:-

$$I_C = \frac{\beta (V_{CC} - 0.7)}{R_B + (1 + \beta) R_E} \approx \frac{V_{CC} - 0.7}{(R_B/\beta) + R_E}$$

It is tempting to say that because β is large R_B/β is negligible but we cannot do that because R_B is, itself, large (usually low hundreds of kΩ). If this was the case the final expression for I_C would be independent of β which would be highly desirable. However there is a *tendency* for variations in transistor β is be "ironed out".

The emitter resistor is supplying *feedback* to the circuit. The gain of the circuit is much less than that of the same circuit without R_E but the AC gain is, to a fair extent, predictable.

Let's find an approximate expression for the AC gain. We will do this properly later and will improve the accuracy but an arm-waving explanation will do here.

Suppose, first, that the transistor is correctly DC biased. Without this assumption we cannot proceed. Suppose we then raise the voltage on the transistor base by 1mV. Because the voltage from base to emitter is constant at about 0.7V (forward biased diode) the voltage on the emitter must also increase by 1mV. This causes a *change* in the emitter current of $1mV/R_E$.

Now transistor base current is small so $I_E \approx I_C$. Therefore there will be an almost equal *change* in the collector current. Therefore there will be a *change* in the voltage *across* R_C of $(1mV/R_E) * R_C$.

Note that this is an *increase* in the voltage *across* R_C. This corresponds to a *decrease* in the voltage *from the collector to ground*.

The *change* in the output voltage $((-1mV/R_E)*R_C)$ divided by the *change* in the input voltage (1mV) is the *gain*. The AC gain is therefore $-R_C/R_E$, a resistor ratio.

This analysis is not quite correct because it ignores small changes in the approximately 0.7V diode forward voltage and also ignores base current. It works best if R_C/R_E is fairly low (less than 10?).

5.3 COMMON EMITTER SELF BIAS

Shown in Figure 5.5 is a common emitter amplifier with an emitter resistor, R_E, and a *self bias* circuit.

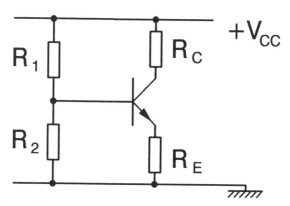

Figure 5.5: Common Emitter Amplifier with Self Bias

Again we should do a little analysis but this time we can draw on what went before. Look at the bias circuit; it is just a potential divider. And potential dividers have a Thenevin equivalent. Using this equivalence the circuit becomes that shown in Figure 5.6.

The voltage V_{BB} is given by:- $V_{BB} = \dfrac{R_2}{R_1 + R_2} V_{CC}$ and

the bias resistor, R_{BB}, $(= R_1 \| R_2)$, is given by:- $R_{BB} = R_1R_2/(R_1 + R_2)$

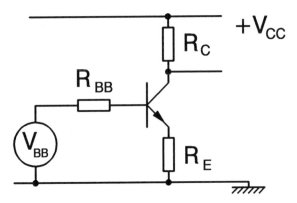

Figure 5.6: Common Emitter Amplifier with Thenevin Equivalent Bias

We can use this in the previous analysis for the fixed bias circuit with emitter resistor to find the base current:-

$$I_B = \frac{V_{BB} - 0.7}{R_{BB} + (1 + \beta) R_E}$$

We can continue from here as before to obtain:-

$$I_C = \frac{\beta (V_{BB} - 0.7)}{R_{BB} + (1 + \beta) R_E} \approx \frac{V_{BB} - 0.7}{(R_{BB}/\beta) + R_E}$$

Now we *can* say that because β is large R_{BB}/β is fairly small and therefore the final expression for I_C is almost independent of β.

We could not say this in the previous case because R_B had to be large to avoid excessive base current. In this case we can make R_{BB} (or, in other words, R_1 and R_2) fairly small without vast base current flowing.

We normally pick the ratio of R_1 and R_2 in such a manner that the voltage on the base of the transistor is, in some sense, optimum. Normally we set this voltage so that the transistor output voltage swing is maximised.

Look at the circuit of Figure 5.5 again. The output voltage swing is set by the maximum and minimum possible values of V_{out}. We should set the quiescent output voltage so that it is mid-way between these two values. When the output voltage is set in this way the transistor collector current, I_C, will also be mid-way between its minimum and maximum

When the transistor is full OFF it will be drawing the minimum collector current, $I_{C(min)}$, which will be equal to zero.

To find $I_{C(max)}$ assume the transistor is hard ON. It will therefore be saturated and will have about 0.3V across it. If there is 0.3V across the transistor there will be $(V_{CC} - 0.3)V$ across R_C and R_E. The current, $I_{C(max)}$, will therefore be:-

$$I_{C(max)} = (V_{CC} - 0.3)/(R_C + R_E)$$

The average collector current, $I_{C(quiescent)}$, will be given by:-

$$I_{C(quiescent)} = (I_{C(max)} + I_{C(min)})/2 = I_{C(max)}/2 \quad \text{since} \quad I_{C(min)} = 0$$

Assuming that $I_C \approx I_E$, the quiescent voltage on the emitter will be:-

$$V_{E(quiescent)} = I_{C(quiescent)} * R_E$$

The quiescent voltage on the base on the base should be set to be 0.7V greater than the quiescent voltage on the emitter. Thus:-

$$V_{B(quiescent)} = V_{E(quiescent)} + 0.7$$

This allows the ratio of R_1 and R_2 to be found.

It is also possible to set the bias point to minimise power dissipation or according to a number of other criteria but maximum output voltage swing is the criterion we will normally use in this book.

THIS FORM OF BIASING IS THE ABSOLUTELY STANDARD TECHNIQUE.

It has all the required advantages of stability and repeatability that we require. The gain of the complete circuit is the same as in the last case, approximately $-R_C/R_E$.

5.4 DESIGN TECHNIQUE

To find the resistor values for the Common Emitter Self Bias circuit, knowing the desired gain, the power supply voltage, V_{CC}, and the value of the transistor β, proceed as follows:-

5.4.1 Find values for R_C and R_E.

The AC gain is given by $-R_C/R_E$. We cannot find appropriate absolute values for these resistors without adding a further constraint.

If we know the desired output impedance of this amplifier then this is approximately equal to R_C.

We may have the quiescent (in this case, average) power dissipation. In this case *do not* try to use equations like I^2/R for the power in the resistors. *The transistor dissipates power too!* Go back to "P = VI". We know the power supply voltage and we know the power dissipated. Thus $I_{C(quiescent)} = P/V_{CC}$. Note that we are ignoring power dissipated in R_1 and R_2 and that due to base current. We will come back to that later.

Now consider how an incoming AC signal would cause I_C to vary. A big input signal could, at its most negative, cause the transistor to cut off. At its most positive it could cause the transistor to go into saturation. The voltage difference between the quiescent output and the minimum should be equal to the voltage between the quiescent output and the maximum. Thus, to allow the maximum, unclipped, symmetric output signal we should set the the quiescent current to be *half* the maximum possible current.

We get $I_{C(max)}$ when the transistor is full ON. When it is full ON $V_{CE} = V_{CE(sat)} \approx 0.3V$. Thus the voltage across R_C and R_E is $(V_{CC} - 0.3)$.

We now know the maximum current through, and the maximum voltage across, R_C and R_E so we can calculate the series resistance of R_C and R_E. The ratio of the two is given by the gain so we can find real values for these resistors.

Example

Gain $= -3.4$, Power ≈ 12mW, $V_{CC} = 15$V.

From the gain we have $R_C/R_E \approx 3.4$. The quiescent current is $(12\text{mW}/15\text{V})$mA so the maximum current is twice this, $(24/15)$mA.

The maximum voltage across R_C and R_E is $(15 - 0.3)$V so $R_C + R_E = 14.7/(24/15)\text{k}\Omega = 9.1875\text{k}\Omega$.

Together with $R_C = 3.4\,R_E$ this gives $R_E = 2.088\text{k}\Omega$ and $R_C = 7.099\text{k}\Omega$.

If we used $R_E = 2\text{k}\Omega$ and $R_C = 6.8\text{k}\Omega$ we would be close enough (12.53mW).

5.4.2 Find quiescent voltages, V_E and V_B

We have values for R_C and R_E. Either find $I_{C(\text{quiescent})}$ as half $I_{C(\text{max})}$ or retrieve the value from the previous step. Then $V_{E(\text{quiescent})}$ is equal to $I_{E(\text{quiescent})} * R_E$ (assuming $I_E \approx I_C$). Therefore $V_B = V_E + 0.7$.

We must now set R_1 and R_2 so that the correct value of V_B is produced. First assume that there is no base current. Then $V_B = V_{CC} * R_2/(R_1 + R_2)$

Once again we do not have sufficient constraints to uniquely assign values to R_1 and R_2. We can just pick "reasonable" values for one and calculate the other, we can try to find appropriate standard values or we could add a further constraint.

A popular "rule of thumb" is that we should set R_1 and R_2 such that the current from the power supply through both R_1 and R_2 is approximately one tenth of $I_{C(\text{quiescent})}$. *Note that this current is not the transistor base current!* Use of this rule can lead to rather low resistor values but it's a good start. If we are going to use this rule, and we know this in advance, we should remember that significant power will then be dissipated in the bias chain. We should take account of this in our initial calculations by making $I_{C(\text{quiescent})}$ ten elevenths (91%) of the value we calculated when ignoring dissipation in the bias chain.

5.4.3 Find standard values

Make R_2 a standard value and calculate R_1. It is most unlikely to be a standard value. Shall we make it the higher standard value or the lower standard value? Initially we assumed no base current which is not actually true. If we used the exact values calculated for R_1 and R_2 we would find that, because of the base current, V_B would be a little low. Let's lessen this error by making R_1 the lower standard value, hence lifting V_B a little.

Example (continued)

We have $I_{C(quiescent)} = (12/15)$mA. Thus

$$V_{E(quiescent)} = (12/15)\text{mA} * R_E = (12/15)\text{mA} * 2\text{k}\Omega = 1.6\text{V}$$

This gives $V_B = 1.6 + 0.7 = 2.3$V.

We have $I_{C(quiescent)} = 0.8$mA so we could set R_1 and R_2 such that one tenth of this value flowed through them. This gives:-

$$15/(R_1 + R_2) = 0.08\text{mA} \Rightarrow R_1 + R_2 = 187.5\text{k}\Omega.$$

To get $V_B = 2.3$V we also need $15\,R_2/(R_1 + R_2) = 2.3$
$\Rightarrow R_1 = 5.52\,R_2$.

Together these give $R_1 = 158.75$kΩ and $R_2 = 28.75$kΩ. These are non-standard values but if we made $R_2 = 27$kΩ, then R_1 should be 165.6kΩ, which can be rounded down to 150kΩ, a standard value.

QUESTIONS

5.1) Design a circuit which is capable of grounding two loads using two NPN transistors. Input A grounds *both* while input B grounds only *one*.

5.2) For the circuit in Figure 5.7 calculate the collector voltage for transistor gain (β) values of 10, 50, 100 and 200 ($V_{CE(sat)}$ = 0.3 volts).

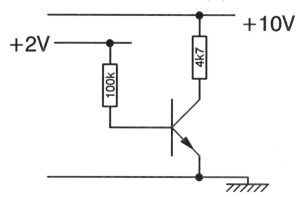

Figure 5.7: Transistor with fixed bias

5.3) Calculate the approximate DC bias voltages at all points in the circuit shown in Figure 5.8 given that β = 50 and $V_{CE(sat)}$ = 0.3 volts.

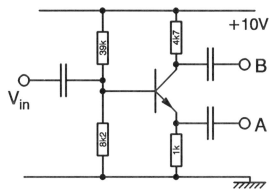

Figure 5.8: Self Biased Transistor Amplifier

Chapter 6

TRANSISTOR SMALL SIGNAL ANALYSIS

Thus far we have considered transistor operation, biasing and bias stability. Now we can assume that the DC biasing is correct and concentrate on the AC performance.

Transistors are not particularly linear devices and non-linear circuit analysis is *very* difficult. We *linearise* the system by introducing a *small-signal model*. We assume that in a very small region about the bias point the (non-linear) characteristics of the transistor can be approximated by a *linear* function.

In graphical terms we are assuming that the transistor characteristics near the bias point are equal to the tangent to the real characteristics at that point. Take for example the graph of V_{BE} against I_C shown in Figure 6.1.

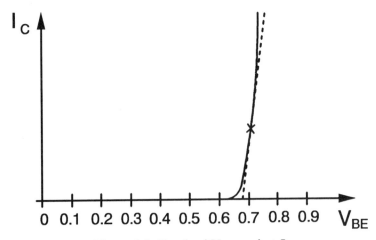

Figure 6.1: Graph of V_{BE} against I_C

This is basically an exponential graph (as I_C is proportional to I_B which is proportional to $e^{qV_{BE}/mkT}$). Assuming the bias point is as marked we will assume the graph about the bias point is the tangent (as shown).

Such techniques can be considered a bit "dirty" but *either* input signals are very small *or* there is lots of feedback which always sorts things out!

6.1 TRANSISTOR SMALL-SIGNAL MODEL

Basic Assumptions:-

1)   DC conditions are correct

2)   Variations about the quiescent point are so small that the transistor can be considered a *linear* device.

We will use the h-PARAMETER MODEL.

The argument for this model goes as follows:-

1) V_{BE} is a function of I_B and V_{CE} (through the Early effect). Therefore:-

$$V_{BE} = f_1(I_B, V_{CE})$$

2) I_C is a function of I_B and V_{CE}. Therefore:-

$$I_C = f_2(I_B, V_{CE})$$

Taking Taylor Series expansion and neglecting the higher order terms gives:-

$$\Delta V_{BE} = \left.\frac{\delta f_1}{\delta I_B}\right|_{V_{CE}} \Delta I_B + \left.\frac{\delta f_1}{\delta V_{CE}}\right|_{I_B} \Delta V_{CE}$$

$$\Delta I_C = \left.\frac{\delta f_2}{\delta I_B}\right|_{V_{CE}} \Delta I_B + \left.\frac{\delta f_2}{\delta V_{CE}}\right|_{I_B} \Delta V_{CE}$$

where ΔV_{BE} is a small change in V_{BE} and

$\left.\dfrac{\delta f_2}{\delta I_B}\right|_{V_{CE}}$ is the partial differentiation of f_2 with respect to I_B *while holding V_{CE} constant.*

We use lower case to represent small changes in a variable, so for example, $\Delta V_{BE} = v_{BE}$.

Let $\quad h_{ie} = \left.\dfrac{\delta f_1}{\delta I_B}\right|_{V_{CE}} \qquad$ *input resistance*

$\quad\quad h_{re} = \left.\dfrac{\delta f_1}{\delta V_{CE}}\right|_{I_B} \qquad$ *reverse transfer voltage ratio*

$\quad\quad h_{fe} = \left.\dfrac{\delta f_2}{\delta I_B}\right|_{V_{CE}} \qquad$ *forward transfer current ratio* $\to \beta$

$\quad\quad h_{oe} = \left.\dfrac{\delta f_2}{\delta V_{CE}}\right|_{I_B} \qquad$ *output conductance*

Then $\qquad\qquad\qquad\qquad v_{BE} = h_{ie}\, i_B + h_{re}\, v_{CE} \quad$ and

$$i_C = h_{fe}\, i_B + h_{oe}\, v_{CE}$$

This is known as the *hybrid* model because h_{re}, h_{fe} have no units, h_{ie} is in ohms and h_{oe} is in Siemens. Note that h_{fe} is, as near as makes no odds, β.

The "e" part of the subscript is because all these variables refer to the common Emitter collection. In theory there are another two groups of h-parameters which are for the common Base and common Collector configurations but we will not worry about these differences here.

The equation $v_{BE} = h_{ie}\, i_B + h_{re} v_{CE}$ can be represented by the circuit shown in Figure 6.2 and the equation $i_C = h_{fe}\, i_B + h_{oe} v_{CE}$ can be represented by the circuit shown in Figure 6.3.

Note that in both cases the units analyse dimensionally correctly.

Combining these two gives us the h-parameter small signal model for the transistor shown in Figure 6.4.

Note that this is a *model* of a transistor which has the useful property that it fits with the maths we find possible to carry out. It is only one of many possible models, all of which have different trade-offs between accuracy and complexity. *It is part of the work of a designer to decide what accuracy, and therefore what complexity, is required for a particular task.*

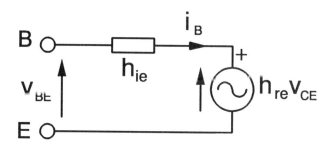

Figure 6.2: Circuit for $v_{BE} = h_{ie} i_B + h_{re} v_{CE}$

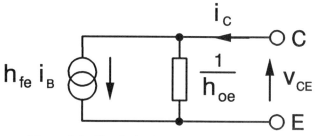

Figure 6.3: Circuit for $i_C = h_{fe} i_B + h_{oe} v_{CE}$

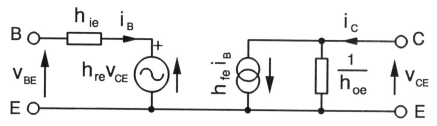

Figure 6.4: h-parameter Small-Signal Model for a Transistor

The model given is sometimes a little too complex for our needs. If we examine typical values for the four h-parameters we find that h_{re} and h_{oe} tend to be small. Sometimes we find that we can neglect them in which case the model we use reduces to that shown in Figure 6.5.

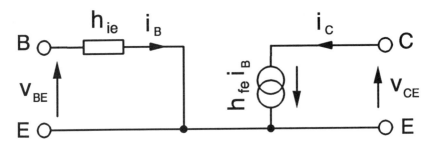

Figure 6.5: Reduced Small Signal Model for a Transistor

6.2 USING SMALL SIGNAL TRANSISTOR MODELS

When converting a real circuit diagram into a small-signal model we always go through the following steps:-

1. Call all static voltages ground

We are interested only in AC signals. Any circuit nodes that don't "move", i.e. have on them static DC voltages, are AC ground. Take, for example, the circuit shown in Figure 6.6.

There is one guaranteed static, DC, voltage in the circuit, V_{CC}. It can be considered to be provided from an *enormous*, precharged, capacitor (like a battery) and therefore has negligible AC impedance to ground. To AC signals, V_{CC} is ground. This is shown in Figure 6.7.

2. Short-Circuit any Decoupling Capacitors

Decoupling capacitors are components which serve to decouple, i.e. separate, AC and DC signals. In the circuit under consideration they isolate the driving and driven stages (the ones before and after our circuit) from the bias conditions of our CE stage. They pass AC and stop DC. They are therefore replaced by *short-circuits* in our AC model.

BEWARE, not all capacitors are decoupling capacitors. Decoupling capacitors are BIG and are clearly meant to pass all AC signals. Small capacitors must

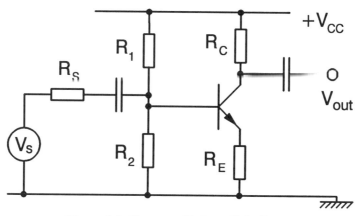

Figure 6.6: Common Emitter Gain Stage

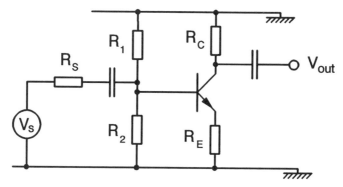

Figure 6.7: CE Gain Stage with DC Voltages Grounded

stay in the model as small capacitors. A capacitor can be considered a decoupling capacitor if, compared to the rest of the circuit, its impedance is low *at the frequencies of interest*. This definition is rather vague but, as always, it is all a question of the degree of accuracy required. If you are not sure whether a capacitor qualifies leave it in the model and analyse the circuit using the phasor techniques explained later.

This stage passed, we have the circuit of Figure 6.8.

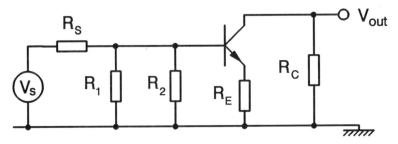

Figure 6.8: CE Stage with Decoupling Capacitors Short-Circuited

3. Replace the Transistor with the Model

The only problem left is the transistor itself. This we must replace with our *linearised* small-signal model as shown in Figure 6.9.

Note that we replace the actual transistor with the model pin by pin. Thus the emitter terminal of the model goes *exactly* where the emitter of the transistor was and the base connection of the model goes *exactly* where the base connection of the transistor was. Same for the collector.

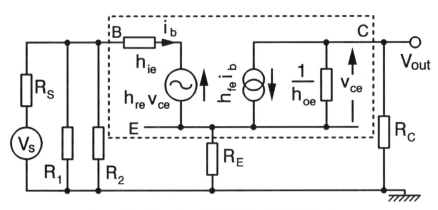

Figure 6.9: Complete AC Model of CE Gain Stage

Do *not*, for example connect the model emitter to earth unless the transistor emitter was connected to earth.

4. Tidy up

In this case this involves tidying up the input network. We have one AC source, v_s, driving into the transistor, R_1, R_2 and R_s. We could find a Thenevin equivalence for this little input network such as that shown in Figure 6.10 with

$$v_T = \frac{R_1 \parallel R_2}{(R_1 \parallel R_2) + R_s} v_s \quad \text{and} \quad R_T = R_1 \parallel R_2 \parallel R_s$$

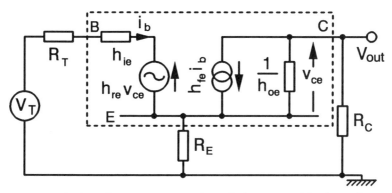

Figure 6.10: AC Model of Transistor Gain Stage with Thenevin
Equivalent Input Stage

However, it is probably more helpful to simply merge R_1 and R_2 into a single resistor $R_B = R_1 \| R_2$ and, otherwise, leave the circuit alone. This is shown in Figure 6.11.

To proceed further with the analysis using this model is perfectly possible but the answers obtained, while fairly accurate, are not in a form which allows us to draw helpful conclusions. We have already observed that this circuit has lots of feedback (the emitter resistor) and that its gain is approximately $-R_C/R_E$. Since we have lots of feedback the finer details of the transistor model are unlikely to have any great effect on the analysis outcome so let's omit them.

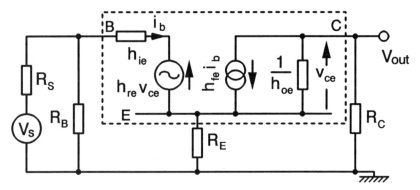

Figure 6.11: AC Model of a CE Gain Stage

Assume that h_{re} and h_{oe} are zero. The AC model of the circuit becomes that shown in Figure 6.12.

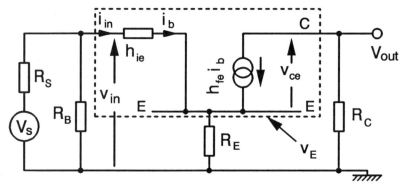

Figure 6.12: Simplified AC Model of CE Amplifier

We can now apply all our techniques of circuit analysis to this problem. In particular we will use Ohm's Law and Kirchoff's Laws. Note that, for now, we will consider our input as being the voltage on the input of this amplifier, v_{in}, marked on Figure 6.12.

Apply Kirchoff's current law to the node marked v_E. This tells us that:-

$$i_B + \beta i_B = v_E/R_E$$

$$\Rightarrow (\beta + 1) i_B = v_E/R_E$$

$$\Rightarrow v_E = R_E (\beta + 1) i_B \tag{1}$$

Ohm's Law, applied to the resistor h_{ie} tells us that:-

$$i_B = (v_{in} - v_E)/h_{ie} \tag{2}$$

Kirchoff's current law, applied to the output node, tells us that:-

$$\beta i_B + v_{out}/R_C = 0 \Rightarrow i_B = -v_{out}/(\beta R_C) \tag{3}$$

(the sum of current *leaving* a node is equal to zero.)

Substituting the first of these into the second gives:-

$$i_B h_{ie} = v_{in} - R_E (\beta + 1) i_B \Rightarrow v_{in} = i_B [h_{ie} + R_E (\beta + 1)] \tag{4}$$

Substituting (3) into (4) gives:-

$$v_{in} = \frac{-v_{out}}{\beta R_C} * [h_{ie} + R_E (\beta + 1)] \tag{5}$$

Rearranging this into the standard form, output/input, gives:-

$$\frac{v_{out}}{v_{in}} = \frac{-\beta R_C}{h_{ie} + (\beta + 1) R_E} \tag{6}$$

Note the particular form of the denominator of this expression. It will turn up again and again.

Note also that if β is very high this expression is equal to $-R_C/R_E$, the expression we arrived at earlier using "arm-waving" techniques. If β is not infinite the actual gain will be rather less than this.

The last thing to note here is that this answer can be partially confirmed using *dimensional analysis*. This technique is so useful that a separate section will be devoted to it in the next chapter.

Let us continue the analysis of the common-emitter gain stage which has the circuit diagram shown in Figure 6.6 and the small-signal equivalent model given in Figure 6.12. We already have that:-

$$\text{Gain} = \frac{v_{out}}{v_{in}} = \frac{-\beta \, R_C}{h_{ie} + (\beta + 1) \, R_E}$$

6.2.1 Input Impedance

We should now consider the transistor input impedance. Note that this does not include the effects of R_1 and R_2. It is defined as:-

$$R_{in(trans)} = v_{in}/i_{in} = v_{in}/i_B$$

To solve this we take equations (1) and (2) from page 55 and eliminate v_E.

This gives:– $$R_{in(trans)} = \frac{v_{in}}{i_B} = h_{ie} + R_E \, (\beta + 1)$$

Note that this in not the input impedance of the whole amplifier. To have a correct DC bias point we must have R_1 and R_2. In small-signal terms these are connected from the transistor input to ground. Thus the whole amplifier input impedance is $R_1 \| R_2 \| R_{in(trans)}$.

In all probability $R_{in(trans)}$ will be fairly high, almost certainly higher than R_1 and R_2. Thus these two resistors in parallel will dominate the amplifier input impedance. For this reason, we would like these two resistors to have the highest possible values. However, optimum DC bias stability occurs when these two resistors have very low values. Thus a compromise must be made between DC bias stability (with varying β, temperature, etc) and amplifier input impedance.

6.2.2 Output Impedance

To find the output impedance we require to force a current from or into the circuit and observe the effect on the output voltage. This can be done with no input signal present; only a DC bias value is required. We can therefore set $v_{in} = 0$.

We will force a small current i_x *into* the circuit output as shown in Figure 6.13.

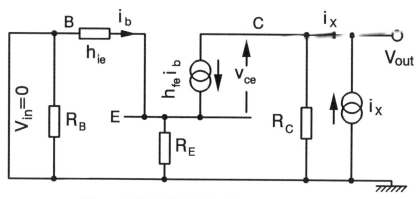

Figure 6.13: AC Model of CE Amplifier showing
Current being forced in the output terminal

Note that, because $v_{in} = 0$, R_B $(= R_1 \parallel R_2)$ is short-circuited to ground. The equations become:-

$$i_B = (0 - v_E)/h_{ie} \tag{1}$$

$$i_x = \beta\, i_B + v_{out}/R_C \tag{2}$$

$$(\beta + 1)\, i_B = v_E/R_E \tag{3}$$

At first we need only consider equations (1) and (3) which, together, state that:-

$$h_{ie}\, i_B = -R_E\, (\beta + 1)\, i_B \tag{4}$$

The only way that this can be true is if $i_B = 0$. Substituting this into equation (2) gives:-

$$i_x = \frac{v_{out}}{R_C} \Rightarrow R_{out} = \frac{v_{out}}{i_x} = R_C \tag{5}$$

Thus the circuit output impedance is equal to the value of the collector resistor, R_C.

6.3 CIRCUIT ANALYSIS, COMMON EMITTER, DECOUPLED EMITTER

Suppose we take the circuit of Figure 6.6 and modify it by adding a big capacitor in parallel with R_E as shown in Figure 6.14. This would not alter the DC bias point of the transistor but would dramatically alter the AC gain.

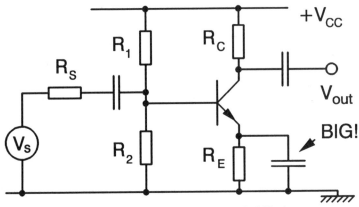

Figure 6.14: CE Gain Stage, Decoupled Emitter

At DC the transistor still has feedback (due to R_E) and this feedback will keep the bias point fairly stable, even with varying β.

To AC signals, the added decoupling capacitor across R_E will be a short circuit so $R_{E(AC)} = 0$. Our simple, arm-waving analysis would then indicate that Gain $= -R_C/R_E = -R_C/0 = \infty$. Obviously this is not going to happen but we can see that the gain is going to be high.

Clearly, the addition of the decoupling capacitor has removed all feedback to AC signals. For this reason, when analysing the circuit, we will have to pay attention to the smaller details of the transistor model. Thus, in this case, we would *not* assume that h_{ie} and h_{re} are zero and we would use the full h-parameter model.

We could obtain the small-signal equivalent circuit as before, but perhaps it would be better to start at Figure 6.10 and short out R_E. This is shown in Figure 6.15.

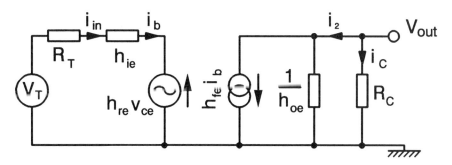

Figure 6.15: Small-signal Equiv. Circuit for CE stage with added emitter decoupling capacitor

Note that now the emitter of the model is grounded.

6.3.1 Current Amplification, A_i

When considering current amplification we view the output current as the small-signal current *in the collector resistor*, R_C. This is i_C.

$$A_i = \frac{i_C}{i_{in}} = \frac{-i_2}{i_{in}}$$

Kirchoff's Current Law applied to the collector node gives:-

$$i_2 = h_{fe} i_{in} + h_{oe} v_{out}$$

Also $$v_{out} = i_C R_C = -i_2 R_C \quad \text{so}$$

$$i_2 (1 + h_{oe} R_C) = h_{fe} i_{in}$$

$$A_i = \frac{-i_2}{i_{in}} = \frac{-h_{fe}}{(1 + h_{oe} R_C)}$$

[As h_{oe} is small, $A_i \approx -h_{fe} \approx -\beta$, which is what we might expect.]

6.3.2 Transistor Input Impedance, Z_{in}

Note that this is the input impedance of the *transistor* and so does not include R_T.

$$Z_{in} = v_{in}/i_{in}$$

Kirchoff's Voltage Laws on the input loop give:-

$$v_{in} = h_{ie} i_{in} + h_{re} v_{out}$$

Now $v_{out} = -i_2 R_C = A_i i_{in} R_C$. Thus:-

$$v_{in} = h_{ie} i_{in} + h_{re} A_i i_{in} R_C$$

This gives $Z_{in} = \dfrac{v_{in}}{i_{in}} = h_{ie} + h_{re} A_i R_c = h_{ie} - \dfrac{h_{re} h_{fe} R_C}{1 + h_{oe} R_C}$

6.3.3 Voltage Amplification, A_v

This is the one in which we are usually interested.

$$A_v = v_{out}/v_{in}$$

Applying Kirchoff's Voltage Law to the input side gives:-

$$v_{in} = i_{in} h_{ie} + h_{re} v_{out}$$

$$\Rightarrow i_{in} = (v_{in} - h_{re} v_{out})/h_{ie} \qquad (*)$$

Applying Kirchoff's Voltage Law to the output side gives:-

$$v_{out} = i_C R_C = -i_2 R_C = -R_c (h_{fe} i_{in} + v_{out} h_{oe})$$

$$\Rightarrow v_{out} (1 + R_C h_{oe}) = -h_{fe} R_C i_{in}$$

With $(*)$ this gives:-

$$v_{out} (1 + R_C h_{oe}) = \frac{-h_{fe} R_C v_{in} + h_{fe} R_C h_{re} v_{out}}{h_{ie}}$$

$$\Rightarrow v_{out}(h_{ie} + R_C h_{oe} h_{ie} - h_{fe} R_C h_{re}) = -h_{fe} R_C v_{in}$$

$$\Rightarrow A_v = \frac{v_{out}}{v_{in}} = \frac{-h_{fe} R_C}{h_{ie} + R_C h_{oe} h_{ie} - h_{fe} R_C h_{re}}$$

There is another, less tiresome method of getting the above result using previously calculated values.

$$A_v = v_{out}/v_{in}$$

$$v_{out} = i_C R_C = A_i i_{in} R_C$$

$$v_{in} = Z_{in} i_{in}$$

These imply $A_v = (A_i R_C)/(Z_{in})$ and if we substitute the already calculated values for A_i and Z_{in} we get the same result.

6.3.4 Voltage Amplification of Complete Circuit

The overall voltage gain of the amplifier is the gain from v_s to v_{out} as defined in Figure 6.6 (but remember that now the emitter is decoupled to ground). Thus

$$Gain = v_{out}/v_s$$

We do not have gain defined in this way. We have other variables v_{in} and v_T. We can therefore rearrange the gain equation to be

$$Gain = \frac{v_{out}}{v_{in}} * \frac{v_{in}}{v_T} * \frac{v_T}{v_s}$$

Clearly this is the same thing, only stretched out a bit. However, we do have all these terms defined somewhere.

v_{out}/v_{in} is something we have just found.

$$\frac{v_{out}}{v_{in}} = A_v = \frac{-h_{fe} R_C}{h_{ie} + R_C h_{oe} h_{ie} - h_{fe} R_C h_{re}}$$

To find v_{in}/v_T we will have to think a little harder. The input side of the circuit is drawn in Figure 6.11 but when looking for v_{in}/v_T we could replace the transistor with its input impedance, Z_{in}, which we have. This is shown in Figure 6.16.

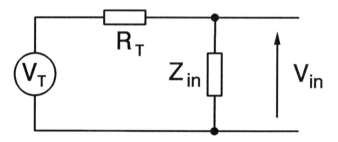

Figure 6.16: CE Transistor Model Input Stage

Clearly
$$v_{in} = \frac{Z_{in}}{R_T + Z_{in}} v_T$$

We also have
$$Z_{in} = h_{ie} - \frac{h_{re} h_{fe} R_C}{1 + h_{oe} R_C}$$

These combine to give the horrendous expression:-

$$\frac{v_{in}}{v_T} = \frac{h_{ie} + h_{oe} h_{ie} R_C - h_{re} h_{fe} R_C}{R_T + h_{oe} R_C R_T + h_{ie} + h_{oe} h_{ie} R_C - h_{re} h_{fe} R_C}$$

The last bit, v_T/v_s we had on page 53 above Figure 6.10. It was:-

$$\frac{v_T}{v_s} = \frac{R_1 \parallel R_2}{(R_1 \parallel R_2) + R_s} = \frac{R_1 R_2}{R_1 R_2 + R_1 R_s + R_2 R_s}$$

All these lovely equations combine to give:-

$$Gain = \frac{-h_{fe} R_C}{R_T + h_{oe} R_C R_T + h_{ie} + h_{oe} h_{ie} R_C - h_{re} h_{fe} R_C} \quad *$$

$$\frac{R_1 R_2}{R_1 R_2 + R_1 R_s + R_2 R_s}$$

This is a perfect example of something which is correct but meaningless! The equations may be exact but they have got out of hand and we can draw no conclusions from them. Now is the time to make some sweeping assumptions.

If we make some assumptions (carefully!) we might well get an answer which is inaccurate but at least we will be able to understand it. After all, what's 10% inaccuracy between friends! The resistors we use may have 5% tolerance, the h-parameters will all have at least 25% tolerance. What's the use of an answer to ten decimal places? We don't have any of the input data to any degree of accuracy.

Let's suppose that R_s is fairly small compared to R_1 and R_2. Then $R_T \approx R_s$ and $v_T \approx v_s$. Then our expression for gain becomes:-

$$\text{Gain} \approx \frac{v_{out}}{v_{in}} \frac{v_{in}}{v_s}$$

We have

$$\frac{v_{in}}{v_s} = \frac{Z_{in}}{Z_{in} + R_s}$$

The expression for gain given a few paragraphs ago, $A_v = A_i R_C/Z_{in}$, is still valid so we have:-

$$\text{Gain} \approx \frac{A_i R_C}{Z_{in}} * \frac{Z_{in}}{Z_{in} + R_s} = \frac{A_i R_C}{Z_{in} + R_s}$$

This is a much nicer looking equation than before. If we also make the approximation that $h_{re} = 0$, which is not unreasonable in this case, and substitute appropriately we get:-

$$\text{Gain} \approx \frac{-h_{fe} R_C}{(h_{ie} + R_s)(1 + h_{oe} R_C)}$$

For normal values of resistance and h_{re} the total error introduced using these approximations is likely to be in the order of 10%.

In almost any analogue circuit using the full models and trying to be accurate will lead to incomprehensible results. It is almost always better to make approximations so that the answer, while less accurate, can be understood and appropriate action can be taken.

6.4 EXTRA EFFECTS

We have now developed and used the h-parameter model for a transistor. However, we must never forget that the four h-parameters are dependent on biasing, transistor processing variations and many other factors.

This chapter is about small-signal analysis and so depends on the h-parameters. These parameters, in turn, depend on large-signal analysis.

Remember the diode equation in Chapter 3, $I = I_s \exp(qV/mkT)$? This related diode current to voltage but applies equally to base current and base-emitter voltage in a transistor. Remembering that $I_C = \beta\, I_B$, we get:-

$$I_C = \beta\, I_s \exp(qV_{BE}/mkT) \quad \textbf{the Ebers–Moll Equation}$$

- Applying a little algebra to the Ebers-Moll equation shows us that increasing V_{BE} by $\ln(10) * mkT/q = 2.3 * 52\text{mV} = 120\text{mV}$ will increase I_C by a factor of *ten*.

  We see that transistors are *highly* voltage dependent; that is the collector current changes *radically* when the base-emitter voltage changes.

- It is possible to find an approximate value for h_{ie} from the Ebers-Moll equation. h_{ie} is, in effect, the input resistance of the transistor so if we can find dV_{BE}/dI_B we will have h_{ie}. Using the diode equation we obtain:-

$$h_{ie} \approx \frac{dV_{BE}}{dI_B} = \frac{mkT}{qI_B}$$

  Because of the particular form of the Ebers-Moll equation, the fact that $I_C = \beta\, I_B$ and $mkT/q = 52\text{mV}$, this also implies that:-

$$h_{ie} \approx \frac{mkT}{qI_C} \approx \frac{52}{I_C} \quad \text{where} \quad I_C \text{ is in mA}$$

- Let's try changing *temperature*. We cannot do this through the Ebers-Moll equation because I_s, far from being constant, is *extremely* dependent on temperature. I_s roughly *doubles* for every $8{\to}10°C$ rise in temperature.

As I_s varies the collector current varies. Alternatively, we can reverse the thought processes and say that if we are to keep the collector current *constant* as temperature changes we must vary V_{BE}. In fact, we should *reduce* V_{BE} by about 2.1mV for every 1°C *rise* in temperature if I_C is to be held constant.

- Early Effect. We cannot derive tis from the Ebers-Moll equation; it is caused by the effective width of the base changing and the collector-emitter voltage varies. It is given by:-

$$\Delta V_{BE} \approx -0.001 \, \Delta V_{CE}$$

The Early Effect is particularly important when designing current sources.

If we bear these extra effects in mind we should be in good shape to design some real transistor circuits.

QUESTIONS

6.1)   The circuit in Figure 6.17 (same as Figure 5.8, page 45) is fed with a 1kHz signal from a low impedance source which modulates the transistor base by ±90mV. Calculate and plot the approximate output voltages at points A and B *without* using the h-parameter small signal model.

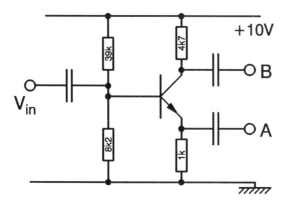

Figure 6.17: Self Biased Transistor Amplifier

6.2)   Draw the h-parameter small signal equivalent circuit of the amplifier
       shown in Figure 6.17. Use the equivalent circuit to calculate the AC
       power gain of the amplifier in at 1kHz if h_{ie} = 1kΩ, h_{re} = h_{oe} = 0
       and h_{fe} = β = 50. The output power is the AC power dissipated in
       R_C which *itself* is the load.

       By finding the AC gain of the amplifier and then using *large-signal*
       calculations to discover the limits on the output voltage at point B,
       calculate   the   maximum   input   voltage   that   this   amplifier   can
       accommodate without distortion.

6.3)   The   emitter   resistor, R_E,   used   in   the   amplifier   circuit   shown   in
       Figure 6.17 is decoupled to ground with a 100μF capacitor. Draw the
       h-parameter small signal equivalent circuit of the amplifier. Use the
       equivalent circuit to calculate the AC power gain of the amplifier in at
       1kHz if the h-parameter values are as given in question 6.2.

       Calculate the maximum input voltage that this AC amplifier can
       accommodate without distortion. Is this an exact calculation?

6.4)   Find new component values for the circuit of Figure 6.17 such that the
       amplifier has a gain of approximately -3, dissipates between about 25
       and 35mW and is biased such that its output voltage swing is
       maximised. Use standard resistor values throughout. What is the
       effect on the circuit gain if 5% resistors are used?

6.5)   Which common transistor configuration is illustrated in Figure 6.18
       and in what application is it used? Draw the small signal h-parameter
       equivalent circuit. If h_{fe} = 100 and h_{ie} = 1kΩ what is the small signal
       input resistance, r_{in} which is defined as r_{in} = v_{in}/i_B.

       What is the voltage gain, v_o/v_S, when the circuit is fed from a voltage
       source with an internal impedance of 100 kΩ. In this question assume
       that the bias chain resistors shown are not actually present (implying
       that, in reality, the biasing is being carried out by the DC bias of the
       driving circuit).

6.6)   The transistor collector in Figure 6.17 is connected to the transistor
       base of the circuit in Figure 6.18. R_a and R_b are absent. What is the
       voltage gain of this new amplifier?

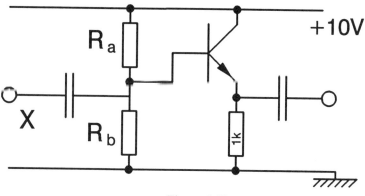

Figure 6.18

6.7) Design a simple common emitter amplifier with a gain of ten which will drive an eight ohm load (like a loudspeaker). Use a 10V power supply. To maximise efficiency (!) place the loudspeaker in the collector lead so that it acts as R_C. Bias the transistor for maximum output voltage swing. Calculate the quiescent power dissipated in the loudspeaker, R_E and the transistor. What is the maximum possible AC power that can be dissipated in the loudspeaker? Comment on the efficiency of this system.

6.8) Consider the circuit shown in Figure 6.19. Calculate DC bias points. Using Ohm's Law and $V = L(di/dt)$ find an expression for the gain of this amplifier. Sketch the input and output waveforms to show the phase shift from input to output.

6.9) In the circuit of Figure 6.20 what value of R_E gives a gain of ten? Calculate the transistor collector quiescent voltage. How would you find the correct base bias voltage? Comment on the probable efficiency of this amplifier compared to the one in Problem 6.7.

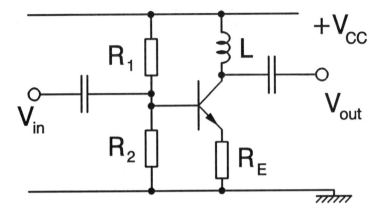

Figure 6.19: Common Emitter Amplifier with inductor in place of R_C

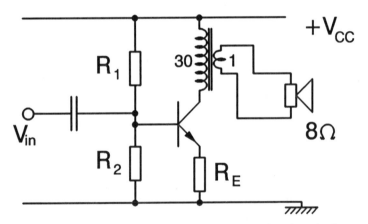

Figure 6.20: CE Amplifier to drive 8Ω load (loudspeaker)
using transformer

Chapter 7

DIMENSIONAL ANALYSIS

Dimensional analysis is an extremely useful technique which can help us reject some incorrect solutions to problems as impossible. Put somewhat facetiously, it says that problem solutions of the type

$$5 \, Cows \; = \; 37 \, Oranges$$

are wrong. The technique simply involves examining the *units* of each side of the equation are checking whether they are consistent. It is probably easiest to explain by example.

1) $V_{out} = I_{in}/R_4$ is wrong. The left hand side (LHS) has units of volts while the right hand side (RHS) has units (volts ohms^{-2}).

2) $V_{out} = V_{in} + I_{in}$ is wrong. The RHS is volts plus current and these cannot be added directly.

3) $V_{out}/V_{in} = -45 \, R_3$ is wrong. The LHS is dimensionless while the RHS is Ohms.

4) $V_{out}/V_{in} = -45 + V_2/(I_{in} \, R_3)$ *might* be correct. Dimensional analysis can only tell you if something is wrong, it cannot say something is definitely correct.

Now try the problems on the next page.

PROBLEMS

A number of students, of varying abilities, have come up with the following
solutions to problems. Here "q" is electron charge, "t" is time in seconds and
"C" is a capacitance. Using dimensional analysis indicate those which are
definitely wrong.

7.1) $V_{out} = I_{in} R_{in} + V_{CC} + 3R_2$

7.2) Input Impedance $= V_{in}/I_{in}$

7.3) Output Impedance $= I_3 R_2 t / q$

7.3) $V_{out} = h_{ie} I_{in} + R_C$

7.4) $V_{out}/V_{in} = (C_1 + C_2)/C_3 - (V_2 C_6)/(I_{out} t)$

7.5) $I_{out} = V_{out}/h_{oe}$

7.6) Output admittance $= I_{out}/V_3$

7.7) Output voltage for op-amp $= 10mA * 150k\Omega$

7.8) $t_1 = V_4 C_4 I_6 - R_4 C_5$

7.9) $t_1 = V_4 C_4/I_6 + 2t_2$

7.10) $t_1 = V_4/C_4 I_6 - 5t_1$

7.11) $t_1 = V_4 C_4/I_6 + 3t_2 C_6$

7.12) $C_4 = t_4/R_3 - q/V_3$

7.13) $t_1 = V_4 C_4 / I_6 + R_3 C_7$

7.14) $V_{out} = (R_3 - R_2)q/C_4$

7.15) Transistor collector current, $I_C, = 100V * 470\mu F/0.1\mu s$

In a University course, its associated exams and in real life an answer to a
problem which is correct according to simple dimensional analysis (and is also
sensible) will be treated with much more respect than one which is not.

Chapter 8

GAIN in dB

Gain is expressed as a ratio of *Power* levels P_1 (usually input) and P_2 (usually output).

$$\text{Gain} = \frac{P_2}{P_1}$$

Over the years engineers have found it convenient to work with logarithmic scales rather than linear scales. If circuits are cascaded gains have to be multiplied. Multiplication is a difficult operation; engineers prefer addition. If gains are expressed in logarithmic terms multiplication becomes addition. (There are a number of other advantages!)

To this end the "Bel" was introduced. This is $\log_{10}$ of the power ratio. Therefore gain can be given as:-

$$\text{Gain} = \log_{10}(P_2/P_1) \ \text{Bel}$$

This came up with inconvenient numbers so, instead, we use the deciBel which is, not surprisingly, one tenth of a Bel. Gain is conventionally given in dB (deciBels) as:-

$$\text{Gain}_{dB} = 10 \log_{10}\left[\frac{P_2}{P_1}\right]$$

Now Power into a resistor is V^2/R so

$$\text{Gain}_{dB} = 10 \log_{10}\left[\frac{V_2^2/R_2}{V_1^2/R_1}\right] = 20 \log_{10}\left[\frac{V_2}{V_1}\right] \quad \textbf{IF } \mathbf{R_1 = R_2}$$

In practice the restriction that R_1 should equal R_2 appears to have disappeared and *usually* we can get off with defining a voltage ratio in dB as:-

$$\text{Gain}_{dB} = 20\log_{10}[V_2/V_1]$$

Note that gain of a system is *always* given as output/input, never the other way round!

There are a number of particular *voltage* gains which should be committed to memory. These are:-

Linear Gain	Approx. Gain (dB)	Accurate Gain (dB)	Linear Gain	Approx. Gain (dB)	Accurate Gain (dB)
2	6dB	6.0206dB	10	20dB	20dB
3	10dB	9.5424dB	100	40dB	40dB
5	14dB	13.9794dB	1000	60dB	60dB

If you know these values you can work out approximate dB equivalents mentally. For example:-

$150 = 3 * 5 * 10 \rightarrow 10dB + 14dB + 20dB = 44dB$

$8000 = 2 * 2 * 2 * 1000 \rightarrow 6dB + 6dB + 6dB + 60dB = 78dB$

In electronics circuits are frequently cascaded. For example, consider an op-amp comprising three stages, a differential stage with a gain of 50, a gain stage with gain 150 and an output stage with gain 20. The overall system gain would be $50 * 150 * 20$.

If these gains had been expressed in dB we would have had gains of approximately 34dB, 44dB and 26dB, respectively. The overall system gain would then be $34dB + 44dB + 26dB = 104dB$, a much easier piece of arithmetic!

QUESTION

8.1)   Convert the power and voltage gains found in questions 6.2, 6.3, 6.5 and 6.6 (on page 66) to dB.

Chapter 9

COMPLEX NUMBERS

The Complex Number system is an extension to the good old-fashioned Real number system. The extension is made by the introduction of an "imaginary" number, the square root of −1. In Mathematics this value is called "i". In Engineering we have already booked "i" for other purposes so we use "j".

$$j = \sqrt{-1}$$

In so far as we cannot find any solid things to count with them, complex numbers do not really exist. For example we cannot find a complex number of bricks! Originally they were a figment of the imagination of some mathematician with nothing better to do, but when they were developed fully it was found that they had a series of properties which modelled rather well things which did arise in the real world. In particular, in Electrical Engineering, they allow us to hold a complete description of an AC signal in a very convenient fashion. To describe an AC signal we need to know:-

1) Amplitude

2) Frequency and

3) Phase

All these can be held conveniently in a complex number.

A general complex number is made up of two parts, the *real part* and the *imaginary part*. Thus, for a general complex number, z,

$$z = (a + bj)$$

Note that "a" and "b" are REAL numbers.

We often draw the so-called complex number plane as shown in Figure 9.1

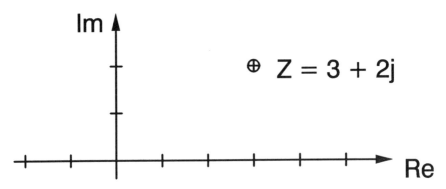

Figure 9.1: The Complex Number Plane

The x-axis is renamed the Real-axis and the y-axis is renamed the Imaginary-axis. Shown in Figure 9.1 is a complex number $z = (3 + 2j)$. It is a single point on the complex plane.

There are a number of operations which are defined for complex numbers and these are discussed in the following sections.

9.1 NORMAL ARITHMETIC OPERATIONS

In this bit let $z_1 = a_1 + b_1 j$ and $z_2 = a_2 + b_2 j$. Remember that a_1, a_2, b_1 and b_2 are REAL numbers.

Addition: $-$ $z_1 + z_2 = (a_1 + a_2) + (b_1 + b_2)j$

Subtraction: $-$ $z_1 - z_2 = (a_1 - a_2) + (b_1 - b_2)j$

Multiplication: $-$ $z_1 * z_2 = (a_1 + b_1 j) * (a_2 + b_2 j)$

$$= (a_1 a_2 - b_1 b_2) + (a_1 b_2 + a_2 b_1)j$$

Note the negative sign in the real term. This is because the last bit in the real term is $(b_1 j)(b_2 j)$ which, because $j^2 = -1$, is equal to $-b_1 b_2$.

Division

Division is harder to carry out in complex number form. What we do is multiply by the inverse. Thus we work out z_2/z_1 as $z_2 * (z_1)^{-1}$. This means that we must find $(z_1)^{-1}$. We can show that:-

$$(z_1)^{-1} = (a_1 + b_1 j)^{-1} = \frac{1}{a_1^2 + b_1^2} (a_1 - b_1 j)$$

The first part of this is $(\text{Modulus}(z_1))^{-2}$ and the second part is the *conjugate* of z_1 (see later).

9.2 REAL PART

The real part of $z = (a + bj)$ is a. Thus the real part of $z = (3 + 5j)$ is 3.

Taking the real part of a complex number z is denoted by:-

$$\textbf{Re(z)}$$

9.3 IMAGINARY PART

The imaginary part of $z = (a + bj)$ is b. Thus the imaginary part of $z = (3 + 5j)$ is 5.

Taking the imaginary part of a complex number z is denoted by:-

$$\textbf{Im(z)}$$

Note that the imaginary part of a complex number, Im(z), is a REAL number.

9.4 MODULUS

The modulus of a complex number is the "distance" from that number on the complex plane to the origin, 0. Thus, if $z = (a + bj)$,

$$\textbf{mod(z)} = \sqrt{a^2 + b^2}$$

Taking the modulus of a complex number z is denoted by:- $| z |$

The modulus of z = (−3 + 4j) is shown in Figure 9.2 and, in this case, equals 5.

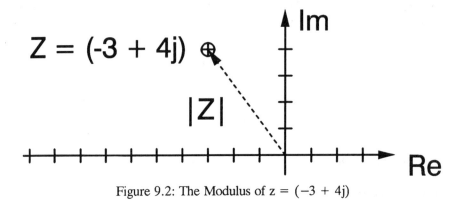

Figure 9.2: The Modulus of z = (−3 + 4j)

9.5 ARGUMENT

If a line is drawn from the complex number on the complex plane and the angle is measured from the x-axis to that line, that angle is the *argument* of the number.

The argument of z = (−2 + 5j) is shown in Figure 9.3.

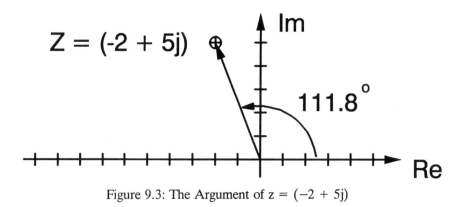

Figure 9.3: The Argument of z = (−2 + 5j)

Mathematically, $\text{Arg}(z) = \tan^{-1}[\text{Im}(z)/\text{Re}(z)]$.

Beware that $\tan^{-1}(x)$ has two answers and we must pick the correct one. Consider $z = (-2 + 5j)$ as shown in Figure 9.3. The argument of z, Arg(z), is equal to $\tan^{-1}(5/-2) = -68.2°$ if plugged into a calculator. However, if we consider where z is on a complex plane we see that the argument should be between 90° and 180°. In fact, the true argument is $-68.2° + 180° = 111.8°$. If you take "tan" of this angle you will get -5/2. Watch out for this catch!

9.6 CONJUGATE

The conjugate of a complex number, $z = a + bj$ is simply $a - bj$.

9.7 COMPLEX EXPONENTIAL

Clearly, we can specify a complex number in two ways.

1) We can give the Real and the Imaginary part (like Cartesian coordinates) or

2) We can give the Modulus and Argument (like Polar coordinates)

There is also a third method which we will use a great deal. We can use a *complex exponential*. An example of a complex exponential is:-

$$z = |z|\, e^{j\phi} \quad \text{where } \phi = \text{Arg(z)}$$

The complex number $e^{j\omega t}$ is shown in Figure 9.4.

In this course we will frequently use the complex exponential form of complex numbers. For this reason we should be comfortable with both forms of complex number ($e^{-j\phi}$ and $a + bj$) and should be able to convert between them quickly.

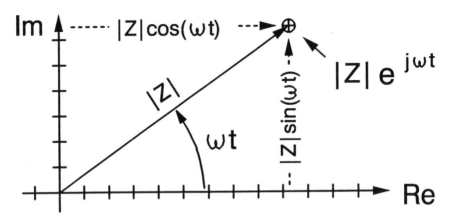

Figure 9.4: The point $e^{j\omega t}$ on the Complex Plane

9.8 CONVERTING BETWEEN CARTESIAN AND COMPLEX EXPONENTIAL

We have a complex number in the form $z = a + bj$ and we need it in the form $z = \alpha e^{j\phi}$.

Now $\phi = \text{Arg}(z) = \tan^{-1}(b/a)$ and $\alpha = |z| = \sqrt{a^2 + b^2}$.

We then have $z = \alpha e^{j\phi}$ as required.

9.9 CONVERTING BETWEEN COMPLEX EXPONENTIAL AND CARTESIAN

We have a complex number in the form $z = \alpha e^{j\phi}$ and we want it in the form $z = a + bj$.

A quick consideration of Figure 9.4 with $\phi = \omega t$ and $\alpha = |z|$ and using the appropriate trigonometry with a right-angled triangle shows that:-

$$a = \alpha \cos(\phi) \quad \text{and} \quad b = \alpha \sin(\phi)$$

9.10 EULER'S THEOREM

Euler's Theorem states that:-

$$e^{j\omega t} = \cos(\omega t) + j\sin(\omega t)$$

This is a mathematical fact, we are not going to attempt to prove it! If you feel an irresistible desire to do so, it is fairly easily done through an examination of the power series for exp, cos and sin.

9.11 COROLLARIES TO EULER'S THEOREM

There are some corollaries to Euler's Theorem which should be stated:-

$$e^{-j\omega t} = \cos(\omega t) - j\sin(\omega t)$$

$$e^{j\omega t} + e^{-j\omega t} = 2\cos(\omega t)$$

$$\Rightarrow \cos(\omega t) = [e^{j\omega t} + e^{-j\omega t}]/2$$

Similarly, $\qquad \sin(\omega t) = [e^{j\omega t} - e^{-j\omega t}]/2j$

Also $\qquad \cos(\omega t) = \mathrm{Re}[e^{j\omega t}] \quad$ and $\quad \sin(\omega t) = \mathrm{Im}[e^{j\omega t}]$

Note that the modulus of $e^{j\omega t}$ is always equal to one.

What is $j\,e^{j\omega t}$?

$$j e^{j\omega t} = j\cos(\omega t) + j^2\sin(\omega t)$$

$$= -\sin(\omega t) + j\cos(\omega t)$$

$$= \sin(\omega t + 180°) + j\cos(\omega t)$$

$$= \cos(\omega t + 90°) + j\sin(\omega t + 90°)$$

This is equivalent to *a rotation by 90°*. Therefore, in general, multiplying a complex exponential by "j" rotates it in the complex plane by 90°. This is shown in Figure 9.5.

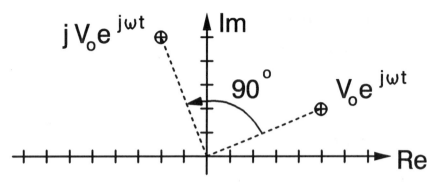

Figure 9.5: Multiplication of Complex Exponential by "j"

QUESTIONS

9.1) Find the polar (trigonometric) form of the following complex numbers given in cartesian (rectangular) form. (a) $4 + j7$, (b) $3 - j5$, (c) 4 and (d) $-j2$. **NB.** $j = \sqrt{(-1)}$

9.2) Find the cartesian (rectangular) form of the following complex numbers given in polar (trigonometric) form.

(a) $2e^{j120}$
(b) $4e^{-j150}$,
(c) $6e^{j90}$
(d) $2e^{-j180}$

NB. All angles are in degrees.

9.3) Find the cartesian form of the sum $z_1 + z_2$ given that:

(a) $z_1 = 3e^{j30}$, $z_2 = 4e^{j60}$
(b) $z_1 = 5e^{j60}$, $z_2 = 2e^{j120}$.

Illustrate your solutions graphically.

Chapter 10

PHASORS

A *phasor* is a vector of constant length, one end of which is fixed to the origin of the complex plane. Further, a phasor is a vector which *rotates* about the origin at a constant rate. Because $e^{j\omega t}$ is a point on the complex plane we can call the line joining the origin and $e^{j\omega t}$ a phasor.

We can draw pictures of phasors like those in Figure 10.1.

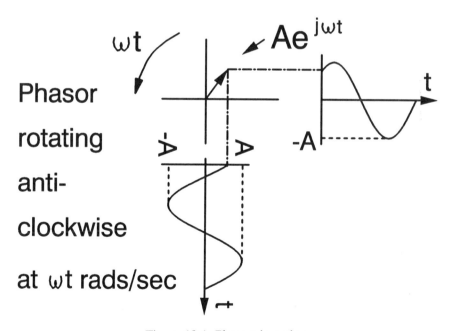

Figure 10.1: Phasors in action

The phasor is the arrow drawn from the centre of the circle to the circumference. *It rotates at ω rads/sec* so what is shown in Figure 10.1 is just a "snapshot" of the phasor at some particular moment in time.

If we project the "x-coordinate" of the phasor, which is its real part, and draw it out over time we get the sine wave shown in the lower half of Figure 10.1. If we project the "y-coordinate" of the phasor, which is its imaginary part, and draw it out over time we get another sine wave as shown towards the right of Figure 10.1.

These two sine waves are identical except they are phase shifted by 90°. One (the real part) is $\cos(\omega t)$ and the other (the imaginary part) is $\sin(\omega t)$. Thus a single phasor holds two real signals and so two complete sets of signal amplitude, frequency and phase information.

10.1 ADDING PHASORS

We are often asked to add signals which are sine waves of the same frequency but different phases and amplitudes. Normally this is a tricky task but phasors make it easy. Shown in Figure 10.2 are two sine waves which are to be added.

At the top of the figure are shown two phasors the real parts of which would produce the two sine waves shown on the left. A vector addition of the two phasors is then carried out and the real part of the sum is projected as the sine wave on the right. This projection is the sum of the two original sine waves.

10.2 CIRCUIT ANALYSIS USING
DIFFERENTIAL EQUATIONS

Consider the circuit shown in Figure 10.3.

Given that $v_s(t) = v_0 \sin(\omega t)$, we can apply Kirchoff's Voltage law to this to obtain:-

$$v_s(t) = v_L + v_R + v_C$$

$$\Rightarrow v_s(t) = L\frac{di}{dt} + iR + v_C$$

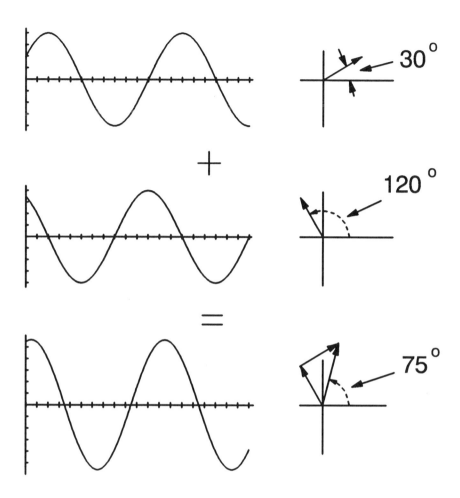

Figure 10.2: Addition of Two Sine Waves using Phasors

Differentiating both sides and substituting for $v_s(t)$ gives:-

$$\frac{dv_s(t)}{dt} = L\frac{d^2i}{dt^2} + R\frac{di}{dt} + \frac{dv_C}{dt}$$

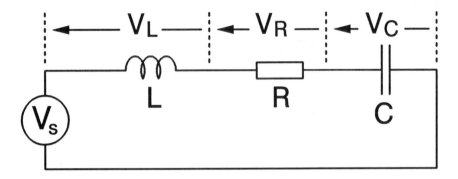

Figure 10.3: RLC Series Circuit

Now, by the standard equations for the capacitor:-

$$i(t) = C\frac{dv_C}{dt} \implies \frac{dv_C}{dt} = \frac{i(t)}{C}$$

Therefore

$$\frac{dv_s(t)}{dt} = L\frac{d^2i}{dt^2} + R\frac{di}{dt} + \frac{i(t)}{C} \tag{1}$$

Now this system is *linear* so the principle of *superposition* applies. If the input was actually the sum of two signals, x and y, we could find the output for input x, OP(x), and the output for input y, OP(y), and sum these to get the output when the input was (x+y). Therefore the final output would be OP(x) + OP(y).

This idea works here too. Our input signal is $v_o \sin(\omega t)$ which can be represented in terms of complex phasors as:-

$$v_o \sin(\omega t) = v_o [e^{j\omega t} - e^{-j\omega t}]/2j$$

Therefore our real input signal, $v_o \sin(\omega t)$, can be represented as the sum of two imaginary signals, or phasors:-

$$v_s^+(t) = v_o e^{j\omega t}/2j \quad \text{and} \quad v_s^-(t) = -v_o e^{-j\omega t}/2j$$

Now these signals, $v_s^+(t)$ and $v_s^-(t)$, are not proper signals we could see on an oscilliscope. They are mathematical "funnies" which don't really exist. However, they are of a form (exponential) which is very useful when working with differential equations. If we find the current in the circuit when each of these odd signals is input and sum the results we should get a real current which we could measure. We will have used the "unreal" signals as mathematical tools to help us get a real answer.

Since $\quad v_s^+(t) = v_o\, e^{j\omega t}/2j$, we have $\qquad \dfrac{d\,v_s^+(t)}{dt} = \tfrac{1}{2}\omega\, v_o\, e^{j\omega t}$

Also $\quad v_s^-(t) = -v_o\, e^{-j\omega t}/2j$, so $\qquad \dfrac{d\,v_s^-(t)}{dt} = \tfrac{1}{2}\omega\, v_o\, e^{-j\omega t}$

We will substitute $dv_s(t)/dt = dv_s^+(t)/dt$ in equation (1) and find the solution, $i^+(t)$. We will then substitute $dv_s(t)/dt = dv_s^-(t)/dt$ in equation (1) and find the solution, $i^-(t)$.

The grand total solution, $i(t)$, will be the sum of these partial solutions.

For the first part, using equation (1) and remembering that the right hand side of (1) is the *differential* of $v_s(t)$, we have the equation

$$\frac{dv_s^+(t)}{dt} = \tfrac{1}{2}v_o\,\omega\, e^{j\omega t} = L\frac{d^2i}{dt^2} + \frac{di}{dt}R + \frac{i(t)}{C} \qquad (2)$$

Take as our "guess" for the solution $i^+(t) = k^+\, e^{j\omega t}$, where k^+ is a complex number. Then:-

$$\frac{di^+(t)}{dt} = k^+ j\omega\, e^{j\omega t} \quad \text{and} \quad \frac{d^2i^+(t)}{dt^2} = -k^+\omega^2 e^{j\omega t}$$

The equation becomes:-

$$\left[-\omega^2L + Rj\omega + 1/C\right]k^+ e^{j\omega t} = \tfrac{1}{2}v_o\omega\, e^{j\omega t}$$

This gives $k^+ = \dfrac{\omega\, v_o/2}{-\omega^2L + Rj\omega + 1/C} = \dfrac{v_o/2}{-\omega L + Rj + 1/C\omega}$

Now this solution holds for $dv_s(t)/dt = \frac{1}{2}v_o\,\omega\,e^{j\omega t}$.

For the other part, when $dv_s(t)/dt = \frac{1}{2}v_o\,\omega\,e^{-j\omega t}$, we just repeat the exercise and get

$$k^- = \frac{v_o/2}{-\omega L - Rj + 1/C\omega}$$

Let z^+ be $(-\omega L + Rj + 1/C\omega)$ and z^- be $(-\omega L - Rj + 1/C\omega)$.

Then $\qquad\qquad\qquad k^+ = \dfrac{v_o/2}{z^+} \qquad$ and $\qquad k^- = \dfrac{v_o/2}{z^-}.$

Note that z^+ and z^- are conjugate so $|z^+| = |z^-| = |z|$ and $\mathrm{Arg}(z^+) = -\mathrm{Arg}(z^-) = \phi$.

Therefore we can write z^+ and z^- as:-

$$z^+ = |z|\,e^{j\phi} \text{ and } z^- = |z|\,e^{-j\phi}$$

We now get $\qquad i(t) = \dfrac{v_o}{2}\left[\dfrac{e^{j\omega t}}{|z|\,e^{j\phi}} + \dfrac{e^{-j\omega t}}{|z|\,e^{-j\phi}}\right]$

$$= \frac{v_o}{|z|}\left[\frac{e^{j(\omega t - \phi)} + e^{-j(\omega t - \phi)}}{2}\right]$$

$$\Rightarrow i(t) = \frac{v_o}{|z|}\cos(\omega t - \phi)$$

Now "z" is a complex number but $|z|$ and $\mathrm{Arg}(z) = \phi$ are real numbers that can be calculated knowing R, L, C and ω. Therefore the above expression represents a real current flowing round the circuit and we have the required answer.

10.3 CIRCUIT ANALYSIS USING PHASORS

Suppose we have a *linear* circuit, apply a complex exponential input, $v_0 e^{j\omega t}$ and obtain a complex output, z.

If the actual input is $v_0 \cos(\omega t)$, which is the real part of $v_0 e^{j\omega t}$, the actual output will be the real part of z, Re(z).

If the actual input is $v_0 \sin(\omega t)$, which is the imaginary part of $v_0 e^{j\omega t}$, the actual output will be the imaginary part of z, Im(z).

In our case we could apply an input $v_0 e^{j\omega t}$. The actual input is $v_0 \sin(\omega t)$ which is the *IMAGINARY PART* so the real output will be the *IMAGINARY PART* of the solution.

Taking the previous example and going through the same sort of algebra as before but with an input of $v_0 e^{j\omega t}$ gives:-

$$i(t) = \frac{j v_0}{-\omega L + R j + 1/C\omega} e^{j\omega t}$$

Letting $z = -\omega L + R j + 1/C\omega$ gives:- $i(t) = j \dfrac{v_0}{z} e^{j\omega t}$

Now $1/z = (1/|z|^2)\bar{z}$, where $\bar{z}$ is the complement of z. This implies:-

$$\frac{1}{z} = \frac{1}{|z|^2}\bar{z} = \frac{1}{|z|^2}\overline{(|z| e^{j\phi})} = \frac{1}{|z|^2}|z| e^{-j\phi} = \frac{1}{|z|}e^{-j\phi}$$

where $\phi = \text{Arg}(z) = -\text{Arg}(\bar{z})$

The final solution is therefore:-

$$i(t) = \frac{1}{z} j v_0 e^{j\omega t} = \frac{1}{|z|}e^{-j\phi} j v_0 e^{j\omega t} = \frac{j v_0}{|z|}e^{j(\omega t - \phi)}$$

Taking the imaginary part of the solution gives:-

$$i(t) = \frac{v_0}{|z|}\cos(-\phi + \omega t) \quad \text{as before.}$$

Chapter 11

AC THEORY

11.1 IMPEDANCE OF A CAPACITOR

For a capacitor we have the standard equation:-

$$i_c(t) = C\frac{dv_c(t)}{dt}$$

If we force the voltage across the capacitor to be a phasor or, in other words,

$$v_c(t) = v_0 e^{j\omega t} \qquad \text{then}$$

$$i(t) = Cj\omega v_0 e^{j\omega t}$$

The *impedance* of the capacitor is given by $Z = V/I$ so

$$Z_c = \frac{v_0 e^{j\omega t}}{Cj\omega v_0 e^{j\omega t}} = \frac{1}{j\omega C} = \frac{-j}{\omega C}$$

We can draw the appropriate phasor diagram as shown in Figure 11.1.

We *pick* an angle for the phasor for i_c, in this case on the x-axis. It need not be there, it could be at *any* angle. (Since a phasor rotates constantly around the origin, picking an angle is just a case of taking a "snap-shot" at a particular moment of time.) We have $v_c = i_c Z_c$ so the phasor for v_c is the i_c phasor multiplied by $(-j)$ which corresponds to a rotation of *minus* 90°. It is also multiplied by $(1/\omega C)$ which corresponds to a change in modulus (length).

The two sine waves for voltage and current are also drawn in Figure 11.1 and, strange to say, we see that current leads voltage by 90°.

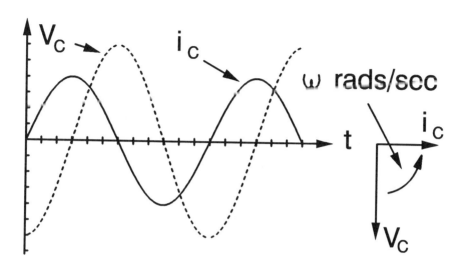

Figure 11.1: Phasor Diagram for current and voltage through a capacitor.

11.2 IMPEDANCE OF INDUCTOR

For an inductor we have the standard equation:-

$$v_L(t) = L\frac{di_L(t)}{dt}$$

This can be rewritten:-

$$i_L(t) = (1/L)\int v_L(t)dt$$

If we force the voltage across the inductor to be a phasor or, in other words,

$$v_L(t) = v_o e^{j\omega t}$$

then

$$i_L(t) = (v_o/Lj\omega)e^{j\omega t}$$

The *impedance* of the inductor is given by $Z = V/I$ so

$$Z_L = \frac{v_o e^{j\omega t}}{(v_o/Lj\omega)e^{j\omega t}} = Lj\omega$$

We can draw the appropriate phasor diagram as shown in Figure 11.2.

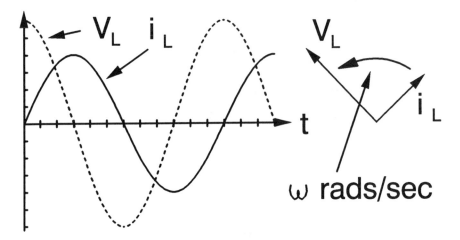

Figure 11.2: Phasor Diagram for current and voltage through an inductor.

As before we *pick* an angle for the phasor for i_L, in this case at angle of about 45° angle. We have $v_L = i_L Z_L$ so the phasor for v_L is the i_L phasor multiplied by (j) which corresponds to a rotation of *plus* 90°. It is also multiplied by (ωL) which corresponds to a change in modulus (length).

The two sine waves for voltage and current are also drawn in Figure 11.2 and we see that voltage leads current by 90°.

11.3 USE OF COMPLEX IMPEDANCES

11.3.1 R-C Series Circuit

Consider the R-C series circuit shown in Figure 11.3.

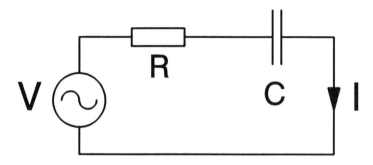

Figure 11.3: R-C Series Circuit

Complex impedances add just like resistances (though the "j" bits require a *little* thought). Therefore the grand total impedance presented to the voltage source by the resistor and the capacitor is:-

$$Z = R + 1/j\omega C$$

If the voltage source gives $v_0 \cos(\omega t)$ we note that this is the real part of $v_0 e^{j\omega t}$ and make that our input, V.

Since $I = V/Z$ we have:- $I = \dfrac{v_0 e^{j\omega t}}{R + (1/j\omega C)}$

Let "D" be equal to $1/[\,R + (1/j\omega C)\,] = 1/[\,R - (j/\omega C)\,]$

Then $|D| = \sqrt{R^2 + 1/(\omega C)^2}^{\,-1}$ and $\text{Arg}(D) = \tan^{-1}[\,1/(\omega R C)\,] = \phi$

Using these definitions gives:- $I = v_0 e^{j\omega t} * |D| * e^{j\phi}$

Therefore:- $i(t) = \text{Re}[I(t)] = v_0 |D| \cos(\omega t + \phi)$

11.3.2 R-L Series Circuit

Consider the R-L series circuit shown in Figure 11.4.

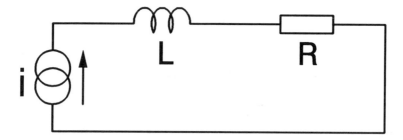

Figure 11.4: R-L Series Circuit

Again the impedances add so $Z = R + j\omega L.$

This time we will draw a phasor diagram (Figure 11.5.)

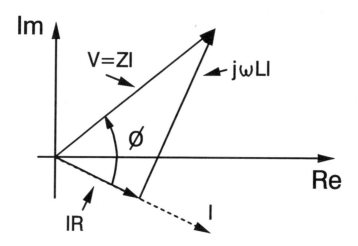

Figure 11.5: Phasor Diagram for R-L Series Circuit

Note that here we are driving the circuit with an **AC** *current source*.

As phasors are constantly whirling round at a rate of ω rads/sec we have had to take the usual "snapshot" and we have caught the current phasor at an angle of about $-25°$. The phasor for voltage across the resistor is in phase with the current phasor so it is on top of it with length IR.

The current through the whole circuit is equal so the *voltage* across the inductor is $v_L = i * Z_L$. Now $Z_L = j\omega L$ so the phasor for v_L is rotated $+90°$ from the current phasor (multiplied by "j") and its length is $\omega L * |i|$.

We add the two voltage phasors together to get the voltage across the R-L combination. We can find the amplitude of the voltage by measuring the length of the voltage sum vector and we can see that the voltage leads the current by an angle ϕ.

We could have done all this work mathematically by following the same principles as for the R-C case just considered.

11.3.3 (Nasty) Example

For the circuit shown in Figure 11.6 you are required to find the currents I_1 and I_2 together with their phases with respect to the input voltage, v_{in}.

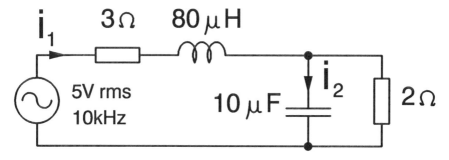

Figure 11.6: Example RLC Circuit.

Solution

First consider v_{in}. It is 5V rms so its peak value is $5\sqrt{2}$. Its frequency is 10kHz but we must have it in rads/sec so $\omega = 2\pi f = 2 * 10^4 \pi$.

We now need the circuit impedances. Let's start with Z_{RC}, the parallel combination of the capacitor and the 2Ω resistor.

We have:- $Z_{RC} = [1/(Z_C) + 1/R]^{-1}$ with $Z_C = 1/j\omega C$

This implies $Z_{RC} = \left[j\omega C + \dfrac{1}{R} \right]^{-1} = \left[\dfrac{(1 + j\omega RC)}{R} \right]^{-1} = \dfrac{R}{1 + j\omega RC}$

Substituting values $(C = 10\mu F, \quad R = 2 \quad \text{and} \quad \omega = 2 * 10^4 * \pi)$ gives:-

$$Z_{RC} = \frac{2}{1 + 1.2566\,j}$$

It would be better it this was in the form $(a + bj)$ so, remembering the rule for complex inverses we get:-

$$Z_{RC} = \frac{2}{1 + 1.2566\,j} = 2 * [1 + 1.2566\,j]^{-1}$$

$$= 2 * \frac{1}{1^2 + 1.2566^2} [1 - 1.2566\,j] = 0.7754 - 0.97446\,j$$

This impedance, Z_{RC}, is in series with the 3Ω resistor and the $80\mu H$ coil.

We have $Z_L = j\omega L = j * 2 * 10^4 * \pi * 80 * 10^{-6} = 5.02655\,j$

The total impedance seen by v_{in} is therefore Z_{tot} where

$$Z_{tot} = 3\Omega + Z_L + Z_{RC} = 3 + 5.02655\,j + 0.7754 - 0.97446\,j$$

$$= 3.7754 + 4.052\,j$$

In a desperate attempt to get away from the complex numbers students often take the modulus of this and try to continue. This is a pity because in doing so they lose all the phase information and so cannot answer the question.

We have that the input is $v_{in} = A \cos(\omega t)$, where $A = 5\sqrt{2}$. Let us instead consider the input to be $V_{in} = A e^{j\omega t}$. Note that our actual input is the REAL part of V_{in}.

We need the current drawn from v_{in} so we use Ohm's Law to get:-

$$I_1 = V_{in} / Z_{tot}$$

Note that at this point we are faced with a division by a complex number which is in cartesian form. This is harder than we would like but, more importantly, if we do the division in cartesian form (multiplying by the inverse) the answer will not be in the right form. We should take this opportunity to convert Z_{tot} into complex exponential form.

We have $Z_{tot} = 3.7754 + 4.052 j$. Its modulus is 5.538 and its argument $(\tan^{-1}(Im/Re))$ is 0.8207 rads/sec. Thus $Z_{tot} = 5.538 e^{0.8207 j}$.

$$I_1 = \frac{V_{in}}{Z_{tot}} = \frac{5\sqrt{2} e^{j\omega t}}{5.538 e^{0.8207 j}} = 1.2767 e^{j(\omega t - 0.8207)}$$

This value, I_1, is complex and what we want is a real value for i_1. Since the actual input is the REAL part of V_{in}, i_1 is $Re(I_1)$. Applying Euler's Theorem to the value for I_1 given above, and taking the real part gives:-

$$i_1 = 1.2767 \cos(\omega t - 0.8207)$$

Thus the magnitude of the current is 1.2767 amps peak, or $1.2767/\sqrt{2} = 0.903$ rms, and it lags the input voltage by 0.8207 rads or 47°.

We now need the current through the capacitor, i_2. We have the total current so we can find the voltage across the $2\Omega \parallel 10\mu F$ combination. We have the impedance of that block, Z_{RC}, but it is in cartesian form. Convert it to complex exponential.

$$Z_{RC} = 0.7754 - 0.97446 j = 1.245354 e^{-0.8986 j}$$

We can now apply this value of Z_{RC} along with Ohm's Law to obtain:-

$$V_{RC} = I_1 * Z_{RC} = 1.2767 \, e^{j(\omega t - 0.8207)} * 1.245354 \, e^{-0.8986 \, j}$$

$$= 1.59 \, e^{(\omega t - 1.71936) \, j}$$

This voltage is across the capacitor so the current through it is:-

$$I_2 = V_{RC}/Z_C = V_{RC}(j\omega C) = V_{RC} * \omega C * e^{j\pi/2} = V_{RC} * 0.62832 * e^{1.57 \, j}$$

Thus $I_2 = 1.59 \, e^{(\omega t - 1.71936 \, j)} * 0.62832 * e^{1.57 \, j} = 0.999 * e^{(\omega t - 0.148565) \, j}$

Taking the real part gives $i_2 = 0.999 * \cos(\omega t - 0.148565)$

11.4 POWER IN AN AC CIRCUIT

Instantaneous power, $P(t)$, is given by:- $P(t) = v(t) \, i(t)$

Average power, P_{av}, is given by:-

$$P_{av} = \frac{1}{T} \int_0^T v(t) \, i(t) dt \qquad \text{where T is the period.}$$

Suppose the voltage and current are out of phase by an angle ϕ. We have:-

$$v(t) = v_o \cos(\omega t + \phi) \quad \text{and} \quad i(t) = i_o \cos(\omega t)$$

Then the average power is given by:-

$$P_{av} = \frac{1}{T} \int_0^T v_o \cos(\omega t + \phi) \, i_o \cos(\omega t) dt$$

Given the angle formula $2 \cos A \cos B = \cos(A - B) + \cos(A + B)$ we can rewrite this as:-

$$P_{av} = \frac{v_o i_o}{2T} \int_0^T \cos(\phi) dt + \frac{v_o i_o}{2T} \int_0^T \cos(2\omega t + \phi) dt$$

$$= \frac{v_o i_o}{2} \cos(\phi) + \frac{v_o i_o}{4T\omega} \left[\sin(2\omega t + \phi) \right]_0^T$$

$$= \frac{v_o i_o}{2} \cos(\phi) + \frac{v_o i_o}{4T\omega} \left[\sin(2\omega T + \phi) - \sin(\phi) \right]$$

$$= \frac{v_o i_o}{2} \cos(\phi) + \frac{v_o i_o}{4T\omega} (0) \quad \text{since } \omega = 2\pi f = \frac{2\pi}{T} \Rightarrow 2\omega T = 4\pi$$

$$= \frac{v_o i_o}{2} \cos(\phi)$$

Here $\cos(\phi)$ is the *power Factor*.

Compare this with another expression for power:-

$$P_{av} = (v_{rms} * i_{rms}) \cos(\phi)$$

$$= \left[\frac{v_{peak}}{\sqrt{2}} * \frac{i_{peak}}{\sqrt{2}} \right] \cos(\phi)$$

$$= \frac{1}{2} (v_{peak} * i_{peak}) \cos(\phi) \quad \text{as before.}$$

11.5 SERIES RESONANCE

Consider the R-L-C series circuit shown in Figure 11.7.

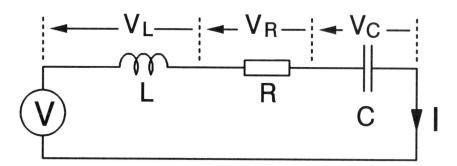

Figure 11.7: R-L-C Series Circuit

The total impedance of the inductor, resistor and the capacitor is:-

$$Z = j\omega L + R + 1/(j\omega C)$$

Clearly, this implies:- $$Z = R + j[\omega L - 1/\omega C]$$

Now, for a given value of R, the modulus of Z will be at a minimum when the imaginary part of Z is equal to zero. At minimum Z maximum current will flow. Also, when the imaginary part is zero, the Argument of Z will be $\tan^{-1}(0) = 0$ so the current and voltage will be in phase. Under these conditions the circuit is said to be in *resonance*. To have a zero imaginary part

$$\omega L = 1/\omega C$$

This gives the resonant frequency in rads/sec, ω_0 as $\omega_0 = 1/\sqrt{LC}$.

Given that ω (rads/sec) is equal to $2\pi f$ we get $f_0 = 1/2\pi\sqrt{LC}$

1) $\omega < \omega_0$

   For input frequencies less than resonance the capacitor presents more impedance than the inductor so in the circuit the current leads the voltage.

2) $\omega = \omega_0$

   For input frequencies equal to the resonance frequency the capacitive reactance cancels the inductive reactance so the circuit is purely resistive. Therefore the current and voltage are in phase.

3) $\omega > \omega_0$

   For input frequencies greater than resonance the inductor presents more impedance than the capacitor so in the circuit the voltage leads the current.

11.6 PARALLEL RESONANCE

Consider the R-L-C parallel circuit shown in Figure 11.8.

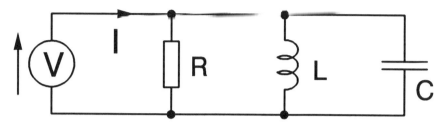

Figure 11.8: R-L-C Parallel Circuit

In this circuit it is more helpful to work with *COMPLEX ADMITTANCE*. Complex admittance, Y, is just the inverse of complex impedance, Z. The units are related as in the following table:-

Impedance (Ohms)	Admittance (Siemens)
R - resistance	G - conductance = 1/R
X - reactance	B - susceptance = 1/X
Z - impedance	Y - admittance = 1/Z

To calculate a value for a parallel combination of components we need:-

$$Z^{-1} = R^{-1} + X_C^{-1} + X_L^{-1}$$

This translates neatly into $\qquad Y = G + B_C + B_L$

This gives:- $\qquad Y = 1/R + j(\omega C - 1/\omega L)$

When the impedance is maximum the admittance is minimum. The minimum admittance arises when:-

$$\omega C = 1/\omega L$$

Therefore there is a resonance at a frequency, ω_0 where:-

$$\omega_0 = \frac{1}{\sqrt{LC}} \text{ rads/sec} \quad \text{or} \quad f_0 = \frac{1}{2\pi\sqrt{LC}} \text{ Hertz}$$

1) $\omega < \omega_0$

For input frequencies less than resonance the inductor presents an easier route for current so in the circuit the voltage leads the current.

2) $\omega = \omega_0$

For input frequencies equal to the resonance frequency the capacitive reactance cancels the inductive reactance so the circuit is purely resistive and $Z = R$ which is its maximum value. Because the circuit is purely resistive at this frequency the current and voltage are in phase.

3) $\omega > \omega_0$

For input frequencies greater than resonance the capacitor presents the easiest route for current so in the circuit the current leads the voltage.

11.7 TRANSIENT RESPONSE

Thus far we have concentrated on the steady-state response of circuits. Most of the time circuits operate in steady-state; that is nothing dramatic has happened (e.g. switch on) for some time. However, circuits must be switched on sometimes and so we need to know how they behave under those conditions.

The importance of switch-on to small circuits is often not that great but there are more serious difficulties in the case of larger circuits like, for example, the national grid. Oscillations can occur in such large systems which blow the insulators off the wall and melt the lines! While such events are interesting, they are not something we should do often.

A typical situation might be where a sine wave produced by an outside source (the grid?) is switched into a circuit. We have the three waveforms shown in Figure 11.9.

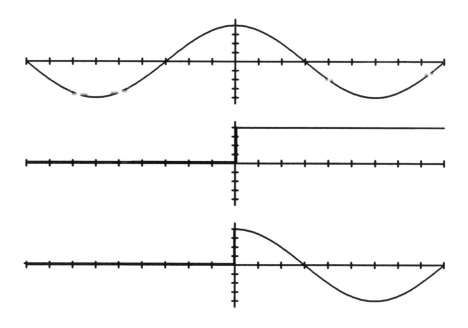

Figure 11.9: Signals involved in Transient Generation

A simple example might be that shown in Figure 11.10 where a capacitor precharged to a voltage V_A is charged/discharged through a resistor R to another voltage V_B.

Intuitively it may be obvious how this system will behave. The result can be found by inspection using a simple change in defined system earth potential. However, it also makes a fair example to attack "properly".

Given that the switch moves from A to B at time t=0, Kirchoff's current laws give:-

$$\frac{V_B - v(t)}{R} = C\frac{dv(t)}{dt} \quad \Rightarrow C\frac{dv(t)}{dt} + \frac{v(t)}{R} = \frac{V_B}{R}$$

This is a **NON-HOMOGENEOUS DIFFERENTIAL EQUATION**.

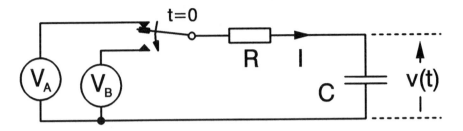

Figure 11.10: Capacitor charging from V_A to V_B

To solve this equation we first find the solution, $v_h(t)$, to the **HOMOGENEOUS** equation:-

$$C\frac{dv(t)}{dt} + \frac{v(t)}{R} = 0$$

This solution is also called the **NATURAL RESPONSE**.

We then find the **STEADY-STATE SOLUTION**, also called the **PARTICULAR SOLUTION** or the **FORCED RESPONSE**. This is the solution when $t \to \infty$ and will be denoted here $v_p(t)$.

The **COMPLETE SOLUTION** is the sum of the natural response, $v_h(t)$, and the particular solution, $v_p(t)$.

We then include the initial conditions to get the final answer.

We will carry out this process for the circuit in Figure 11.10.

1) **Natural Response**

We need the solution to $C\frac{dv(t)}{dt} + \frac{v(t)}{R} = 0$

The solution will be of the form $v_h(t) = A e^{-t/RC}$

2) **Particular Solution or Forced Response**

This is the response after infinite time has gone by. Clearly, in this circuit, after a long time v(t) will be equal to V_B. Therefore

$$v_p(t) = V_B$$

3) **Complete Response**

The complete response is the sum of the natural and forced responses. Thus:-

$$v(t) = v_h(t) + v_p(t) = A\,e^{-t/RC} + V_B$$

4) **Initial Conditions**

At t=0, v(t) = V_A. Substituting this in the complete response gives:-

$$V_A = A\,e^{0/RC} + V_B$$

Therefore A = $V_A - V_B$ and the final solution is:-

$$v(t) = (V_A - V_B)\,e^{-t/RC} + V_B$$

The graph of the response is as shown in Figure 11.11.

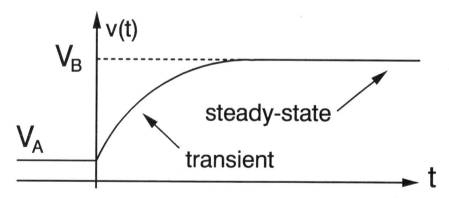

Figure 11.11: DC Transient Response for Circuit in Figure 11.10.

11.7.1 Further Example of Transient Response

In Figure 11.12 an AC signal is switched onto an R-L series circuit at t=0.

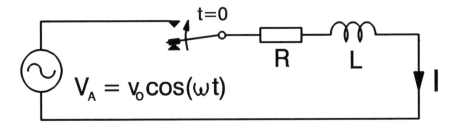

Figure 11.12: R-L Series Circuit driven by Switched AC Voltage Source

1. Apply Kirchoff's Laws

Applying Kirchoff's Voltage law to the circuit for $t \geq 0$ gives:-

$$v_A = v_0 \cos(\omega t) = L\,di/dt + iR$$

2. Find the Natural Response

Find the solution to the homogeneous equation:- $L\,di/dt + iR = 0$

The solution is almost certain to be of the standard sort of exponential form so try $i(t) = A e^{kt}$. Substituting this gives:- $ALk e^{kt} + A e^{kt} R = 0$

This gives $k = -R/L$ so the natural response is:- $i_h(t) = A e^{-Rt/L}$

3. Forced Response

This is the steady state response so it's back to the phasors.

The real circuit input is $v_A = v_0 \cos(\omega t)$ which is the real part of:-
$V_A = v_0 e^{j\omega t}$

Let us input V_A and so find I_A. The real part of I_A will be the natural response.

The total circuit impedance is:- $Z = R + j\omega L$ and $I_A = V_A/Z$ so

$$V_A = v_o\, e^{j\omega t} = I_A\,(R + j\omega L) = I_A\,|Z|\, e^{j\phi}$$

where $Z = (R + j\omega L)$ and $\phi = \text{Arg}(Z) = \tan^{-1}(\omega L/R)$. This gives:-

$$I_A = \frac{v_o\, e^{j\omega t}}{|Z|\, e^{j\phi}} = \frac{v_o}{|Z|}\, e^{j(\omega t - \phi)}$$

The solution we want, $i^P(t)$ is the real part of I_A. Therefore:-

$$i_p(t) = \frac{v_o}{|Z|}\cos(\omega t - \phi).$$

4. Complete Solution

The complete solution is the natural response plus the forced response so:-

$$i(t) = A\, e^{-tR/L} + \frac{v_o}{|Z|}\cos(\omega t - \phi)$$

5. Substitute Initial Conditions

At t=0, i=0. Therefore $A + \dfrac{v_o}{|Z|}\cos(-\phi) = 0$

$$\Rightarrow A = -\frac{v_o}{|Z|}\cos(\phi)$$

Thus $\qquad\qquad i(t) = \dfrac{v_o}{|Z|}\left[\cos(\omega t - \phi) - e^{-tR/L}\cos\phi\right]$

Graphs of the Natural Response, Forced Response and Final Solution are given in Figure 11.13.

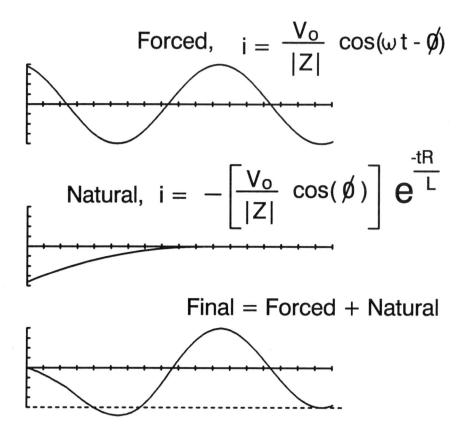

Figure 11.13: Graphs of Natural, Forced and Final Responses
for Circuit of Fig 11.12

11.8 EXAMPLE

Consider the car ignition system mentioned in more detail in Chapter 21, problem 9 (page 224→225). Clearly this is a circuit which is going to operate entirely on its transient response. Also clearly (?) the differential equation is going to be homogeneous because we have only a switched DC voltage; we do not have a forcing AC signal.

Let us consider the primary side of the ignition coil in isolation. In other words, we will pretend the coil secondary, the distributor and the spark plugs are not present. This is, of course, an oversimplification but it makes the whole thing possible for us now. The circuit becomes that shown in Figure 11.14.

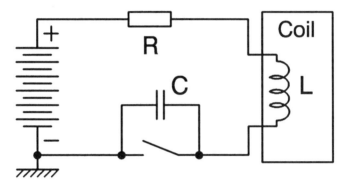

Figure 11.14: Car ignition, primary circuit.

We will assume for t<0 that the contact breaker (switch) is closed and that the current in the coil has built up to its maximum of V/R. At t=0 the switch opens. For t>0 we have a resistor, inductor and capacitor in series across a DC voltage supply, V. Kirchoff's current law leads us to:-

$$\text{Ri} + \text{L}\frac{di}{dt} + \frac{1}{C}\int i\, dt = V$$

We can differentiate this throughout to obtain:− $\text{L}\frac{d^2 i}{dt^2} + \text{R}\frac{di}{dt} + \frac{1}{C}i = 0$

Let $i = A e^{kt}$. This gives:-

$$i = A e^{kt} \; ; \; \frac{di}{dt} = k A e^{kt} \; ; \; \frac{d^2 i}{dt^2} = k^2 A e^{kt}$$

Then $L \dfrac{d^2 i}{dt^2} + R \dfrac{di}{dt} + \dfrac{1}{C} i = 0$

$\Rightarrow L k^2 A e^{kt} + R k A e^{kt} + \dfrac{1}{C} A e^{kt} = 0$

$\Rightarrow L k^2 + R k + 1/C = 0$

$\Rightarrow k = \dfrac{-R}{2L} \pm \dfrac{\sqrt{R^2 - 4L/C}}{2L} = \dfrac{-R}{2L} \pm \left[\left(\dfrac{R}{2L} \right)^2 - \dfrac{1}{LC} \right]^{1/2}$

If $1/LC > (R/2L)^2$, which it will be for the case under consideration, the result will be two complex conjugate roots. Let

$$\omega = \left[\frac{1}{LC} - \left(\frac{R}{2L} \right)^2 \right]^{1/2} \quad \text{and} \quad a = \frac{R}{2L}$$

Then $k = -a \pm j\omega$ which implies $i = A_1 e^{(-a + j\omega)t} + A_2 e^{(-a - j\omega)t}$

Thus $i = e^{-at} [A_1 e^{(j\omega)t} + A_2 e^{(-j\omega)t}]$

At $t=0$, the current through the coil is V/R and at $t=\infty$ the current is zero. The latter condition is not useful because the e^{-at} part of the equation guarantees this anyway. The former tells us that:-

$$A_1 + A_2 = V/R \Rightarrow A_2 = V/R - A_1$$

The further condition required arises from the observation that at $t=0$ the voltage across the capacitor is zero. Thus, at $t=0$,

$$L \frac{di}{dt} + i R = V$$

We have that:− $i = A_1 e^{(-a + j\omega)t} + A_2 e^{(-a - j\omega)t}$

$\Rightarrow R i = R A_1 e^{(-a + j\omega)t} + R A_2 e^{(-a - j\omega)t}$

Also $\quad \dfrac{di}{dt} = A_1(-a + j\omega)\,e^{(-a + j\omega)t} + A_2(-a - j\omega t)\,e^{(-a - j\omega)t}$

$\Rightarrow \quad L\dfrac{di}{dt} = LA_1(-a + j\omega)\,e^{(-a + j\omega)t} + LA_2(-a - j\omega t)\,e^{(-a - j\omega)t}$

Adding, and setting t=0, gives:-

$$\left[L\dfrac{di}{dt} + Ri\right]_{t=0} = LA_1(-a + j\omega) + LA_2(-a - j\omega t) + RA_1 + RA_2 = V$$

With $A_2 = V/R - A_1$ this gives:-

$$LA_1(-a + j\omega) + (LV/R - LA_1)(-a - j\omega) + V = V$$

$$\Rightarrow \quad A_1(2j\omega) = V\left[\dfrac{a}{R} + \dfrac{j\omega}{R}\right]$$

This gives:- $\quad A_1 = \dfrac{V}{2R}\left[1 + \dfrac{a}{j\omega}\right] \quad$ and $\quad A_2 = \dfrac{V}{2R}\left[1 - \dfrac{a}{j\omega}\right]$

Using $e^{j\omega t} = \cos\omega t + j\sin\omega t$ gives:-

$$i = e^{-at}\dfrac{V}{R}\left[\cos\omega t + \dfrac{R}{2\omega L}\sin\omega t\right]$$

Values for R, L and C which are in the correct ballpark for a typical car would be:-

$$R = 6\Omega \; ; \quad C = 1\mu F \; ; \quad L = 3mH$$

Substituting these values in the equation for ω gives

$$\omega = 18230\,\text{rads/sec} \approx 2900\,\text{Hz} \; ; \quad a = 1000 \; ; \quad R/(2\omega L) = 0.0549$$

Thus $\quad i = 2\,e^{-1000t}\left[\cos(18230t) + 0.0549\sin(18230t)\right]$

By some trigonometric jigery-pokery (see page 115) this can be shown to be equal to

$$i = 2.003\,e^{-1000t}\cos(18230t - 0.055)$$

This expression is graphed below as the solid line. Note how it is very "undamped"; the oscillations go on and on. In reality the spark produced at the secondary draws energy from the system and, roughly speaking, this is rather similar to increasing the damping significantly. Shown in the graph is the same oscillating primary current but greatly damped by the extraction of energy due to the spark. Note its much shorter duration. Note also that the rate of change of primary current is still very significant during the first short period. This fact causes the required high secondary voltage.

If the capacitor is omitted all the energy in the circuit goes into making sparks in the contact breakers and burning them out. The current in the primary decreases unevenly and slowly as shown by the jagged line in the graph. The rate of decrease will be too slow to produce a satisfactory secondary spark. Result- the car won't go.

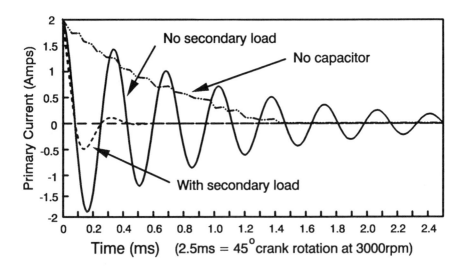

Figure 11.15: Car ignition system primary current.

11.9 EXAMPLE

Consider the circuit shown in Figure 11.16. The capacitor is 10μF and $V_{in} = 4\sin(\omega t)$ with $\omega = 30000$ rads/sec. The switch is opened at t=0. Find the current in the 12Ω resistor.

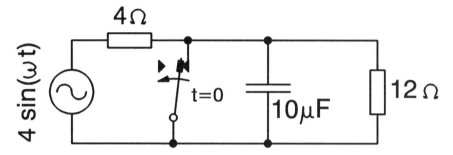

Figure 11.16: R-C Transient Example

Solution

As usual, the first thing to do is *think*! This circuit is not in a particularly desirable form; voltage sources driving series/parallel networks are tricky to work out. However, we could sort things out by applying Thenevin's Theorem to the voltage source and the 4Ω resistor. This transforms the circuit to that shown in Figure 11.17.

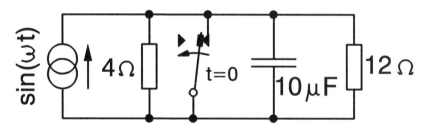

Figure 11.17: Transformed example circuit of Figure 11.16

We then note that we can combine the 12Ω and 4Ω resistors. However, beware! We will eventually require the current in the 12Ω resistor and that will be different from the current in the parallel combination. We can fix this if we aim to find the voltage across the capacitor. Given that, we can calculate the current through a 12Ω resistor which is in parallel with it. If we combine the resistors we get the circuit shown in Figure 11.18.

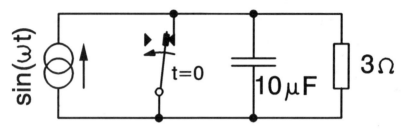

Figure 11.18: Further transformed example circuit of Figure 11.16

It would be perfectly possible to do a Norton-type equivalence on this and get back to a series R-C circuit driven by a voltage source. In fact, that would probably be the sensible thing to do. However, here we will stick with the circuit shown in order to have a current-driven example.

The main differential equation for this circuit is:-

$$i = \sin(\omega t) = \frac{v}{R} + C\frac{dv}{dt}$$

First we solve the homogeneous equation, i.e. $v/R + C\,dv/dt = 0$. Try $v = A\,e^{kt}$.

If $v = A e^{kt}$ then $\dfrac{dv}{dt} = k A e^{kt}$ and

$v/R + C\,dv/dt = 0 \Rightarrow A e^{kt} + RCA k e^{kt} = 0 \Rightarrow k = -1/RC$

Thus we have the usual $v = A e^{-t/RC}$. Remember that this is the voltage on the capacitor. We actually wanted the current through the 12Ω resistor so, given that $i = v/R$, we get:-

$$i(t) = A/12\,e^{-t/RC} = A'\,e^{-33333t} \quad \text{where } A' = A/12$$

Next, using phasors, we go for the forced response. Because we have a parallel circuit we will use admittances (though we needn't explicitly do so). We have:-

$$Y_{in} = j\omega C + 1/R = 0.3333 + 0.3\,j = 0.448\,e^{0.7328\,j}$$

This angle of 0.738 rads/sec is equal to 42°. The input current is the imaginary part of $e^{j\omega t}$ and the voltage is given by $V_C = IZ = I/Y$ so:-

$$V_C = \frac{e^{j\omega t}}{0.448\,e^{0.7328\,j}} = 2.23\,e^{j(\omega t - 0.7328)}$$

and so the voltage across the capacitor, v_C, is given by $2.23\sin(\omega t - 0.7328)$.

What we actually wanted was the current through the original 12Ω resistor so, given that $I = V_C/R$, we get:-

$$I = 2.23/12 * e^{j(\omega t - 0.7328)} * [0.1858 * e^{j(\omega t - 0.7328)}]$$

The actual input was the *imaginary* part of the input phasor so we must take the imaginary part of this answer to obtain:-

$$i(t) = 0.1858\sin(\omega t - 0.7328)$$

The complete response is the sum of the natural and forced responses so

$$i_{complete}(t) = A'\,e^{-33333t} + 0.1858\sin(\omega t - 0.7328)$$

We must now apply the boundary conditions. At t=0 the capacitor was shorted out. Therefore just after t=0 the voltage across the 12Ω resistor would still be zero. Substituting this we get:-

$$i_{complete}(0) = 0 = A' + 0.1858\sin(-0.7328) \;\Rightarrow\; A' = 0.1243$$

Thus, finally, we get:-

$$i_{final}(t) = 0.1858\sin(\omega t - 0.7328) + 0.1243\,e^{-33333t}$$

11.10 A MATHEMATICAL TECHNIQUE

You may have been taught another technique, involving trigonometrical functions, for finding the forced response, that is, the solution to the non-homogeneous equation of the particular integral. This method (which I am *not advocating*) when applied to the example just covered in section 11.9, works out as follows. The equation is:-

$$i = \sin(\omega t) = \frac{v}{R} + C\frac{dv}{dt} \tag{1}$$

Using this technique, one should try the solution:- $v = A\cos(\omega t) + B\sin(\omega t)$. Doing this gives:-

$$v = A\cos(\omega t) + B\sin(\omega t) \quad \text{and} \quad dv/dt = A\omega\sin(\omega t) - B\omega\sin(\omega t) \tag{2}$$

Substituting (2) in (1) gives:-

$$\sin(\omega t) = \frac{A}{R}\sin(\omega t) + \frac{B}{R}\cos(\omega t) + CA\omega\cos(\omega t) - CB\omega\sin(\omega t) \tag{3}$$

Identifying the "sin" and "cos" bits we get:-

$$\frac{A}{R} - CB\omega = 1 \quad \text{and} \quad \frac{B}{R} + CA\omega = 0 \tag{4}$$

These can be solved, using the same values for C, R and ω as before, to give:-

$$A = 1.6574 \quad \text{and} \quad B = -1.4917 \tag{5}$$

We therefore obtain for our particular solution:-

$$v(t) = 1.6574\sin(\omega t) - 1.4917\cos(\omega t) \tag{6}$$

A question very similar to this one was given in a degree exam. Some students attempted this part of it using this method and about a third of them managed to get to this point. However, since what was wanted was the phase shift, this answer was not helpful. No-one managed to continue any further using this technique. But we are better mathematicians than that, aren't we(?). Onward, ever onward.

We know, of course, the old trigonometric identity:-

$$K \sin(\omega t + \phi) = K \cos(\phi) \sin(\omega t) + K \sin(\phi) \cos(\omega t) \qquad (7)$$

Identifying this with equation (6) gives us:-

$$K \cos(\phi) = 1.6574 \quad \text{and} \quad K \sin(\phi) = -1.4917 \qquad (8)$$

Dividing these two into each other gives:-

$$\tan(\phi) = \frac{K \sin(\phi)}{K \cos(\phi)} = \frac{-1.4917}{1.6574} = -0.9 \qquad (9)$$

This gives $\phi = -42°$ *and*, of course, $\phi = 138°$. Which do we take? Assuming that K is positive we know that $\cos(\phi)$ is positive and $\sin(\phi)$ is negative. These observations lead us to $\phi = -42°$ or -0.7328 rads/sec.

Substituting this value for ϕ back into equation (8) gives us K = 2.2298.

Thus $v(t) = 2.2298 \sin(\omega t - 0.7328) \qquad (10)$

We add this to the natural response and continue as before.

Now I am not saying that this technique is wrong. Of course it isn't wrong; it's just inappropriate. It just took four times the column inches of the method using $e^{j\phi}$. Also, it will not work for an RLC network while the $e^{j\phi}$ method works fine. Lastly, phasors will be extensively used in later parts of any Electrical Engineering course. Convinced?

QUESTIONS

11.1) In Figure 11.19 if $R = 10\Omega$, $\omega L = 10\Omega$, $|v| = 100$ volts and the impedance of the capacitor is zero, find the magnitude of the total impedance, the magnitude of the current, i, and voltages v_R and v_L. What is the capacitance of the capacitor?

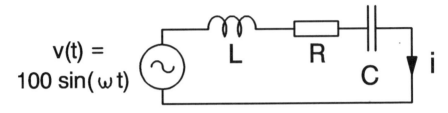

$$v(t) =$$
$$100 \sin(\omega t)$$

Figure 11.19

11.2) If, in Figure 11.19, $R = 100\Omega$, $L = 0.064$ H, $f = 50$ Hz, $|v| = 100$ volts and the impedance of the capacitor is zero, find the magnitude of the total impedance, the magnitude of the current, i, and voltages v_R and v_L and the power factor. Draw a phasor diagram. Repeat for 250 Hz.

11.3) If, in Figure 11.19, $R = 20\Omega$, $L = 0.0318$ H and $C = 80\mu F$, find the impedance and the power factor at 50Hz and 2kHz.

11.4) An R-L-C series circuit has $R = 5\Omega$ and $L = 0.168H$. Calculate the value of capacitance to give resonance at 50 Hz, 1kHz and 1MHz.

11.5) A real capacitor can be modelled by a capacitance in series with a small parasitic inductance. The inductance is due to the connecting wires and the method of construction (which might involve wrapping layers of conductor into a cylinder). Consider the following three capacitors:-

	Capacitor A	Capacitor B	Capacitor C
Capacitance	33pF	0.1μF	4.7μF
Parasitic Inductance	5nH	20nH	50nH

In a real system the capacitors must be connected to the circuit using sections of wire. The approximate rule of thumb for the inductance of straight bits of wire is 1nH per millimetre.

We need to use one of these capacitors to decouple high frequency signals to ground, i.e. we need a capacitor with a low impedance to high frequency signals. In this application the capacitor must have two connecting wires, each 5mm long.

For each of the frequencies (a) 50kHz, (b) 10MHz and (c) 600MHz which capacitor would you use and why? Comment on the practical capacitor impedances at 600MHz.

A student wishes to decouple all frequencies between 50kHz and 600MHz and decides to use a parallel combination of capacitors A and C, each with two 5mm connections, as before. Will this be effective? What will be the combined impedance at 101MHz? What happens at this frequency? How should the decoupling be accomplished?

11.6) It is often necessary to transmit large quantities of power over large(ish) distances. For example, between mainland Scotland and the Outer Hebrides or Shetland. Using overhead cables over these routes presents some practical difficulties so submarine cables are used instead. Such cable can be modelled by a series resistor and inductor connected to a shunt capacitor (shunt ⇒ from the cable to ground). The cable characteristics *per kilometre* are as follows:-

Resistance	0.189Ω
Inductance	$0.344mH$
Capacitance	$0.286\mu F$

In fact, the capacitive component of the cable is the most important and, for now, let's assume the other two values are zero. The maximum current handling capability is 300A.

Suppose we wish to use this cable to supply 33kV to the Outer Hebrides, a distance of, say, 50km. First we lay our cable and we connect it to the national grid. The model will then be that shown in Figure 11.20.

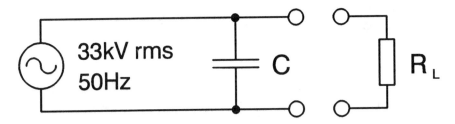

Figure 11.20: Model of Cable

Note that we have not yet connected any load.

What is the magnitude of the voltage at the far end of the cable and what is the magnitude of the current leaving the power station?

Now connect up the load, R_L. Taking account of the maximum current limit of the cable, what is the minimum value of the load resistor? More importantly, what is the maximum power that can be dissipated in a load resistor?

How do these values compare to the values obtained if only a very short bit of cable was required?

Now suppose we must transmit power to the Shetlands which are 100km away (we've moved them for the purposes of this question). What is the minimum value of load resistance and hence the maximum allowable transmitted power? How do these answers compare with the previous set?

What solution do you see to the problem of transmitting large quantities of power over large distances? What further problems can you foresee if we are not connecting a resistive load but are interconnecting two active systems, e.g. the national grids of Britain and France? Can we solve the two problems at once?

11.7) The unknown circuit in Figure 11.21 has response

$$i(t) = \frac{4}{\sqrt{(1 + 4\omega^2)}} \sin(\omega t - \phi) \quad \text{where} \quad \phi = \tan^{-1}(2\omega)$$

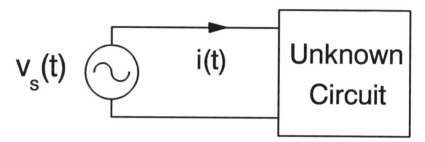

Figure 11.21: Unknown Circuit

What is the complex impedance of the unknown circuit if $v_s(t) = \sin(\omega t)$? Devise a circuit containing one resistor and one inductor which has the same impedance as the unknown circuit. Calculate values for the resistance and the inductance.

11.8) For the circuit illustrated in Figure 11.22, the switch has been in the A position for a long time. Then at time zero ($t = 0$) the switch is moved rapidly to the B position. What is the voltage, $v(t)$, across the capacitor at $t = 0, 0.2, 0.4$ and 1.0 seconds.

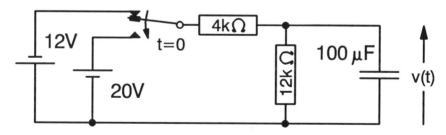

Figure 11.22: Switched R-C Circuit

11.9) For the circuit in Figure 11.23, the switch is closed at time zero. Derive expressions for the natural response, forced response and complete response of the voltage across the capacitor, v(t). You may assume that v(0) = 0V. Sketch your results.

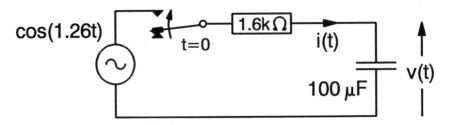

Figure 11.23: R-C Circuit for Transient Analysis

11.10) Consider the circuit shown in Figure 11.24. The inductor is 5mH and $V_{in} = v_o \sin(\omega t)$ with $\omega = 100$ rads/sec. The switch is closed at t=0. Find the current in the coil for $t \geq 0$.

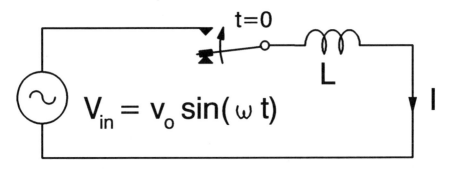

Figure 11.24: Switched voltage source driving inductance

11.11) Consider the circuit shown in Figure 11.25. The capacitor is 10μF and $V_{in} = v_o \cos(\omega t)$ with $\omega = 100$ rads/sec. The switch is closed at t=0. Find the current in the capacitor for $t \geq 0$. Comment.

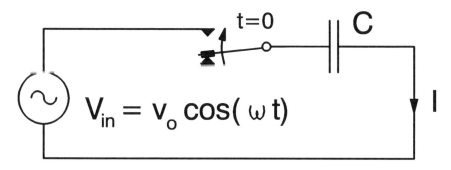

Figure 11.25: Switched voltage source driving capacitor

11.12) You are required to make a bandstop (rejection) filter for insertion
into a transmission line which connects a voltage source of 50Ω
output impedance to a 50Ω load. If the filter is to be resonant at
50Hz and an inductor of 100mH is available with 0.5Ω internal
resistance, select the preferred resonant configuration, calculate the
required value of capacitance and the filter rejection in dB for the
transmission system described above.

Chapter 12

BODE PLOTS

One of the most important frequency sensitive circuits in electronics is the first order low-pass filter. It occurs in many guises throughout circuit design. The very basic structure is shown in Figure 12.1.

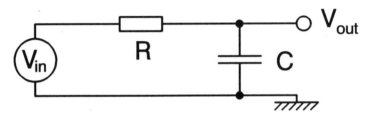

Figure 12.1: Basic First Order R-C Low-Pass Section

The transfer function can be found by thinking of the circuit as a potential divider with a complex impedance present. We have

$$v_{out} = \frac{1/j\omega C}{R + 1/j\omega C} v_{in}$$

Tidying this up gives:-

$$G(\omega) = \frac{v_{out}}{v_{in}} = \frac{1}{1 + j\omega RC} \equiv \frac{1}{1 + j\omega \tau}$$

Note that we have introduced a new variable, τ, and set it equal to RC. τ is the *time constant*.

The amplitude response is given by the modulus of $G(\omega)$.

$$|G(\omega)| = \left|\frac{v_{out}}{v_{in}}\right| = \left|\frac{1}{1 + j\omega\tau}\right| = \frac{1}{\sqrt{1 + (\omega\tau)^2}}$$

We could plot $|G(\omega)|$ against ω but the graph would be messy. It is much better to plot $|G(\omega)|$ **in dB** against **log(ω)**. This form of graph is called a BODE PLOT.

There are two types of BODE PLOT, amplitude and phase. The amplitude Bode Plot is a graph of $|G(\omega)|$ **in dB** against **log(ω)** and the phase Bode Plot is a graph of Arg[$G(\omega)$] against log(ω). The amplitude Bode Plot for our first order section is shown in Figure 12.2.

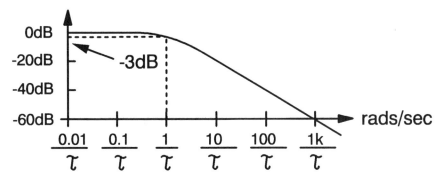

Figure 12.2: Bode plot for a First Order Lowpass Section

Consider the amplitude response of our first order filter at a frequency (in rads/sec) equal to $1/\tau$.

$$|G(1/\tau)| = \frac{1}{\sqrt{1 + [(1/\tau) * \tau]^2}} = \frac{1}{\sqrt{2}}$$

In dB this corresponds to $20\log_{10}(1/\sqrt{2}) = -3$dB. Note the use of "20" in this expression because we are working with a *voltage* ratio, v_{out}/v_{in}.

The frequency $\omega = 1/\tau$ rads/sec is known as the **3dB cutoff point** and marks the **edge of the passband**.

Let us consider the phase response of our first order filter at a frequency (in rads/sec) equal to $1/\tau$.

$$\text{Arg}[G(\omega)] = \tan^{-1}[\text{Im}(G(\omega)/\text{Re}(G(\omega)] = \tan^{-1}[-\omega\tau/1] = -\tan^{-1}(\omega\tau)$$

At $\omega = 1/\tau$, the cutoff frequency, this reduces to $-\tan^{-1}(1) = -45°$.

Note that at $\omega = 0$ $\text{Arg}[G] = 0°$ and at high frequencies, $\omega \to \infty$ $\text{Arg}(G) = -90°$. **The phase response must be between 0° and -90°.**

The **passband** of a circuit is *defined* as the frequency band between the half power points. For a low-pass structure like this, which passes the full signal at DC, the lower cutoff point is zero.

Half power is delivered when the output *voltage* is reduced from its maximum by a factor of $\sqrt{2}$. When the output voltage is thus reduced the output *current* will also be reduced by this factor (Ohm's Law). Therefore the output *power* will be reduced by a factor of $\sqrt{2}^2 = 2 \to$ half power.

The *half power* point is reached when $v_{out}/v_{in} = 1/\sqrt{2}$. In dB, this is -3dB.

In a *bandpass* filter both high and low frequencies are blocked. It therefore has *two* 3dB points and the filter bandwidth is the upper 3dB point minus the lower 3dB point.

12.1 BODE PLOT APPROXIMATIONS - AMPLITUDE

We have:—
$$|G(\omega)| = \frac{1}{\sqrt{1 + (\omega\tau)^2}}$$

Let us consider what happens at high frequencies. If ω is high compared to $1/\tau$ then $\omega \gg 1/\tau$ $= \omega\tau \gg 1$ and

$$|G(\omega)| = \frac{1}{\sqrt{1 + (\omega\tau)^2}} \approx \frac{1}{\sqrt{(\omega\tau)^2}} = \frac{1}{\omega\tau}$$

Suppose we find the amplitude response in dB at a frequency ω_1 which is a good bit higher than $1/\tau$. Then

$$G_{dB}(\omega_1) = 20\log_{10}(1/\omega_1\tau) = -20\log_{10}(\omega_1) - 20\log_{10}(\tau)$$

Let us now consider the amplitude response of the system at a frequency ω_2 which is ten times higher than ω_1. Then $\omega_2 = 10\,\omega_1$.

$$G_{dB}(\omega_2) = 20\log_{10}(1/\omega_2\tau)$$

$$= -20\log_{10}(\omega_2) - 20\log_{10}(\tau)$$

$$= -20\log_{10}(10\,\omega_1) - 20\log_{10}(\tau)$$

$$= -20 - 20\log_{10}(\omega_1) - 20\log_{10}(\tau)$$

$$= -20 + G_{dB}(\omega_1)$$

In other words, as frequency rises by a factor of ten, amplitude decreases by 20dB. This statement is true for input frequencies higher that $1/\tau$.

For input frequencies, ω, significantly *less* than $1/\tau$, i.e. $\omega \ll 1/\tau = \omega\tau \ll 1$ we have:-

$$|G(\omega)| = \frac{1}{\sqrt{1 + (\omega\tau)^2}} \approx \frac{1}{\sqrt{1}} = 1$$

If $|G(\omega)| = 1$, $|G(\omega)|_{dB} = 0$dB. These two straight line approximations are drawn in the amplitude Bode Plot shown in Figure 12.3.

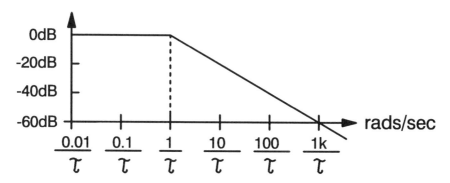

Figure 12.3: Straight line Approximations to Amplitude
Bode Plot for First Order Lowpass

We draw the graph at amplitude 0dB until the cutoff frequency, $1/\tau$, and then draw the line downwards at a slope of -20dB/decade. (A *decade* is a ten-fold increase in frequency).

This straight line approximation to an amplitude Bode Plot is an absolutely standard way of quickly drawing the amplitude response of these structure. *Note that it is an approximation.* The curved line also drawn in Figure 12.3 is the true graph; our straight line approximation is very good away from the cutoff frequency; at the cutoff frequency it is most inaccurate. We have already seen that the graph should be at -3dB at that frequency; the straight line approximation shows 0dB.

At a frequency of $0.1/\tau$ the true amplitude response is -0.04dB; the approximation shows 0dB, not a big error.

At a frequency of $10/\tau$ the true amplitude response is -20.04dB; the approximation shows -20dB, also not a big error.

12.2 BODE PLOT APPROXIMATIONS - PHASE

Figure 12.4 shows the true phase Bode Plot and the straight line approximations we will take.

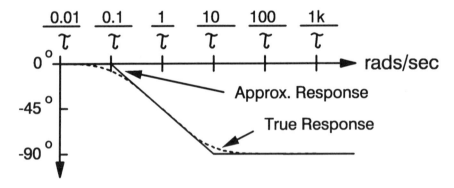

Figure 12.4: True and Approximated Phase Bode Plots
for 1st Order Lowpass

The true phase Bode Plot is just a plot of $-\tan^{-1}(\omega\tau)$. The approximation is:-

$$0° \text{ for } \omega < 0.1/\tau$$
$$-45°/\text{decade for } 0.1/\tau < \omega < 10/\tau$$
$$-90° \text{ for } \omega > 10/\tau$$

Note that the phase is bounded by 0° and −90°. The *amplitude* response after $\omega = 1/\tau$ goes down and down for ever. This is *not* true for the phase response.

Note also that, in the approximate Phase Bode plot, all the action takes place in the decade on either side of $\omega = 1/\tau$.

The maximum error in the approximation to the phase response again occurs at the corners, in other words at $\omega = 0.1/\tau$ and $\omega = 10/\tau$. At these two frequencies the true phase responses are 5.71° and 84.29° so the maximum error is, in modulus, 5.71°.

12.3 BODE PLOTS OF OTHER SIMPLE FUNCTIONS

There are a number of simple functions from which we can construct the Bode Plots of more complex functions.

12.3.1 $G(\omega) = K$ (constant)

Clearly if $G(\omega)$ is a real constant then $|G(\omega)|$ is equal to that same constant. Therefore $|G_{dB}(\omega)| = 20\log_{10}(K)$ and the amplitude Bode Plot is a horizontal line at $20\log_{10}(K)$.

The phase plot is $\tan^{-1}(\text{Im/Re}) = \tan^{-1}(0/K) = 0°$, another straight line.

12.3.2 $G(\omega) = j\omega$

Clearly $|G(\omega)| = \omega$ so $|G_{dB}(\omega)| = 20\log_{10}(\omega)$

At a frequency of 10ω $|G_{dB}(10\omega)| = 20\log_{10}(10\omega) = 20 + 20\log_{10}(\omega)$ so the graph of $G(\omega) = j\omega$ has a slope of +20dB/decade.

Because the graph is a single straight line with a known slope, a single point on the graph completely defines it. If we pick, say, $\omega = 1$ then $G(\omega) = 1$

and $G_{dB}(\omega) = 0dB$. Therefore the graph goes through $1\,rad/sec$, $0dB$.

The phase response is $\tan^{-1}(Im/Re) = \tan^{-1}(\omega/0) = 90°$.

12.3.3 $G(\omega)=(1 + j\omega\tau)$

This function is the inverse of our standard low-pass function. Because $\log(1/x) = -\log(x)$ the amplitude response is the same as that of our low-pass response *only it is flipped across the x-axis* (positive dB becomes negative dB and vice versa).

The phase response is given by $\tan^{-1}(Im/Re) = \tan^{-1}(\omega\tau)$. The argument of the $\tan^{-1}$ function is the inverse of the comparable argument in the low-pass case. Therefore the value of the phase response is negative that of the lowpass case and goes from $0°$ at low frequencies to $+90°$ at high frequencies.

The amplitude and phase Bode Plots for this function are given in Figures 12.5 and 12.6.

12.4 BODE PLOTS OF COMPLEX FUNCTIONS

Often enough, when we find the transfer function of a system we end up with something which does not look too nice. Fairly frequently the only way to get anything meaningful out of the transfer function is to draw a graph and usually the graph we draw is a Bode Plot.

Probably the best way to explain this is by taking an example. Suppose we have:-

$$\frac{v_{out}}{v_{in}} = \frac{2\,j\omega\,(10^4 + j\omega)}{(10 + j\omega)\,(10^7 + j\omega)}$$

The thing to notice here is that this equation comprises five parts, all multiplied together. We could write it as:-

$$\frac{v_{out}}{v_{in}} = \left[2\right]\left[j\omega\right]\left[(10^4 + j\omega)\right]\left[\frac{1}{(10 + j\omega)}\right]\left[\frac{1}{(10^7 + j\omega)}\right]$$

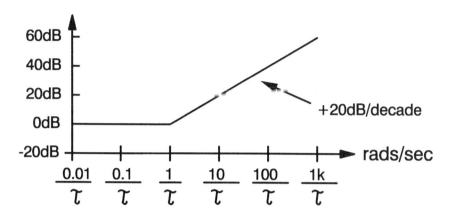

Figure 12.5: Amplitude Bode Plot of $G(\omega) = (1 + j\omega\tau)$

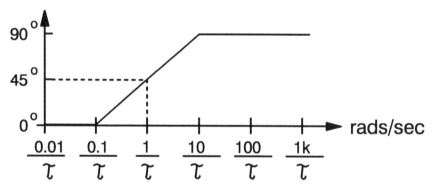

Figure 12.6: Phase Bode Plot of $G(\omega) = (1 + j\omega\tau)$

This looks a bit like a product of our standard simple functions. Let's further mess it about to get:-

$$\frac{v_{out}}{v_{in}} = \left[2\right]\left[j\omega\right]\left[10^4(1 + 10^{-4}j\omega)\right]\left[\frac{10^{-1}}{(1 + 10^{-1}j\omega)}\right]\left[\frac{10^{-7}}{(1 + 10^{-7}j\omega)}\right]$$

Collecting together all the constant terms gives the last rearrangement:-

$$\frac{V_{out}}{V_{in}} = \left[2*10^{-4}\right]\left[j\omega\right]\left[(1 + 10^{-4}j\omega)\right]\left[\frac{1}{(1 + 10^{-1}j\omega)}\right]\left[\frac{1}{(1 + 10^{-7}j\omega)}\right]$$

Now each of these parts are in standard form. We have the following terms:-

1) a constant term, $G_1(\omega) = (2*10^{-4})$,

2) a "jω" term, $G_2(\omega) = j\omega$,

3) a lowpass term, $G_3(\omega) = 1/(1 + \tau_1 j\omega)$ with $\tau_1 = 10^{-1}$

4) an inverted lowpass response $G_4(\omega) = (1 + \tau_2 j\omega)$ with $\tau_2 = 10^{-4}$ and

5) another lowpass term $G_5(\omega) = 1/(1 + \tau_3 j\omega)$ with $\tau_3 = 10^{-7}$.

These are in standard form so we could draw the Bode plot of each. The transfer function is the *product* of the individual terms *but Bode Plots are in dB, a log scale* so the Bode Plot of the whole transfer function is the *sum* of the individual plots.

Let us now draw out the Bode Plot for the constant term, $G_1(\omega)$. First convert the constant to dB. The constant is $2*10^{-4}$ which in dB terms is $20\log_{10}(2*10^{-4}) = -74$dB. The graph is shown in Figure 12.7. The phase plot is a constant $0°$ so we will not draw that!

Next consider $G_2 = j\omega$. This has a slope of $+20$dB/decade. At $\omega = 1$ rad/sec, $|j\omega| = 1 = 0$dB. The amplitude response is therefore as shown in Figure 12.8. As discussed earlier, the phase response is a constant $+90°$ so we will not graph that now.

The next term, $G_3(\omega) = 1/(1 + \tau_1 j\omega)$, is a simple low pass function with cutoff at $1/\tau_1 = 10$ rads/sec. Its amplitude and phase Bode Plots are as shown in Figures 12.9 and 12.10, respectively.

The next term, $G_4(\omega) = (1 + \tau_2 j\omega)$, is an inverted low pass function with cutoff at $1/\tau_2 = 10^4$ rads/sec. Its amplitude and phase Bode Plots are as shown in Figures 12.11 and 12.12, respectively.

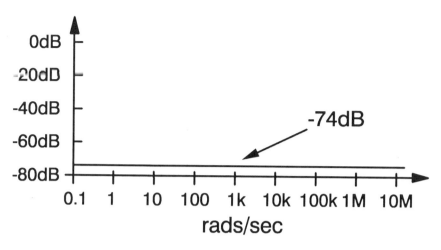

Figure 12.7: Amplitude Bode Plot for $G_1(\omega) = 2 * 10^{-4}$.

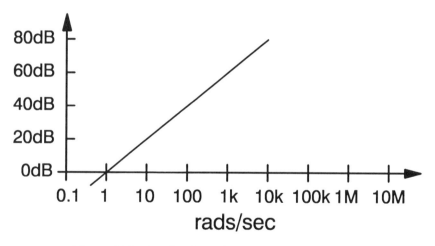

Figure 12.8: Amplitude Bode Plot for $G_2(\omega) = j\omega$.

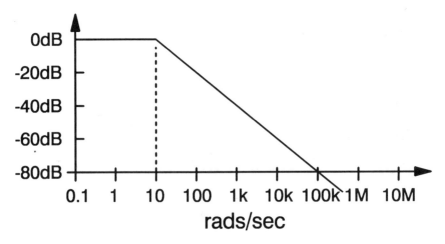

Figure 12.9: Amplitude Bode Plot for $G_3(\omega) = 1/(1 + \tau_1 j\omega)$. $[\tau_1 = 10^{-1}]$

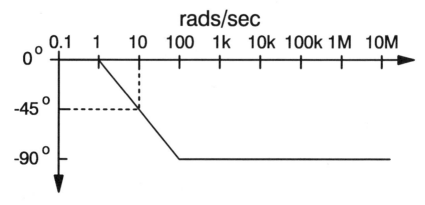

Figure 12.10: Phase Bode Plot for $G_3(\omega) = 1/(1 + \tau_1 j\omega)$. $[\tau_1 = 10^{-1}]$

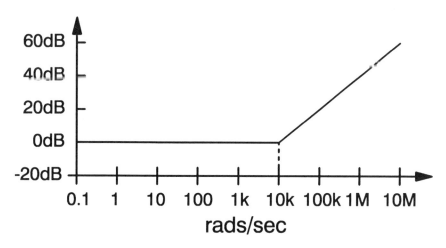

Figure 12.11: Amplitude Bode Plot for $G_4(\omega) = (1 + \tau_2 j\omega)$. $[\tau_2 = 10^{-4}]$

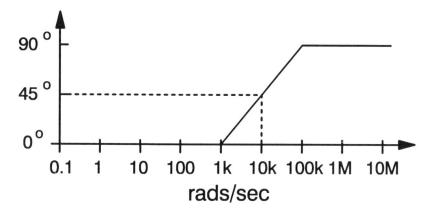

Figure 12.12: Phase Bode Plot for $G_4(\omega) = (1 + \tau_2 j\omega)$. $[\tau_{12} = 10^{-4}]$

The last term, $G_5(\omega) = 1/(1 + \tau_3 j\omega)$, is another simple low pass function with cutoff at $1/\tau_3 = 10^7$ rads/sec. Its amplitude and phase Bode Plots are as shown in Figures 12.13 and 12.14, respectively.

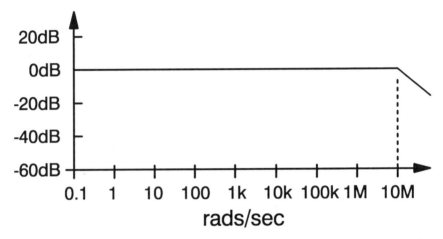

Figure 12.13: Amplitude Bode Plot for $G_5(\omega) = 1/(1 + \tau_3 j\omega)$. $[\tau_3 = 10^{-7}]$

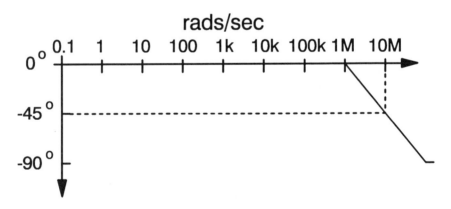

Figure 12.14: Phase Bode Plot for $G_5(\omega) = 1/(1 + \tau_3 j\omega)$. $[\tau_3 = 10^{-7}]$

We must now add these graphs together. Let's first add the terms $G_1(\omega)$ and $G_2(\omega)$. The combined graph will be as shown in Figure 12.15.

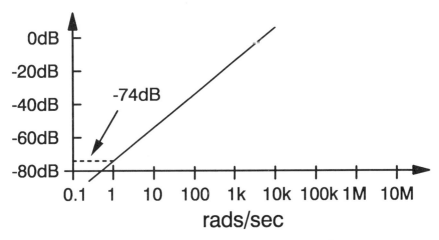

Figure 12.15: Amplitude Bode Plot for $G_1(\omega) = 2 * 10^{-4}$ times $G_2 = j\omega$.

The combined phase response is $0°$ plus $90°$ which is, of course, a constant $+90°$, independent of frequency.

Let us now include the effect of $G_3 = 1/(1 + \tau_1 j\omega)$. The amplitude response of this function is 0dB until the cutoff frequency, 10 rads/sec. It then falls at 20dB/decade. Therefore, in the combined graph, the amplitude response for frequencies up to 10 rads/sec is as for $G_1(\omega)$ times $G_2(\omega)$.

For frequencies of *above* 10 rads/sec the *falling* lowpass response *cancels* the *rising* $j\omega$ response. The final graph therefore rises at 20dB/decade until 10 rad/sec *and is then constant* to infinitely high frequencies. The effect is shown in Figure 12.16.

The phase response of the combination of G_1, G_2 and G_3 is the sum of the individual phase shifts. The combined phase shift for G_1 and G_2 was $+90°$ so we add that amount to the standard lowpass phase response to get the phase response shown in Figure 12.17.

Next add in the effect of G_4. This is an "inverted lowpass" response so its amplitude is constant at 0dB until its "cutoff" when it starts to *rise* at

20dB/decade. In this case the cutoff is 10000 rads/sec so the combined effect of $G_{1\,to\,4}$ is identical to $G_{1\,to\,3}$ at frequencies of up to 10000 rads/sec after which it *rises* at 20dB/decade ever upward to infinite frequencies. The effect is shown in Figure 12.18.

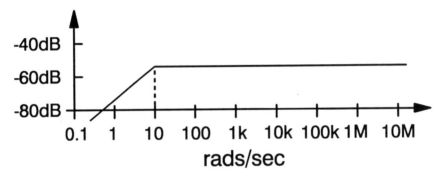

Figure 12.16: Amplitude Bode Plot for $G_1 * G_2 * G_3$.

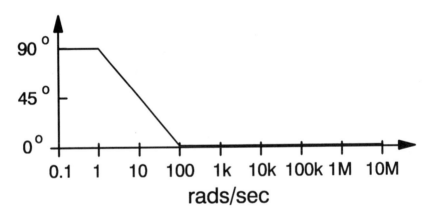

Figure 12.17: Phase Bode Plot for $G_1 * G_2 * G_3$.

The phase plot is identical to $G_{1\,to\,3}$ up to 1000 rads/sec (one tenth of the cutoff frequency of G_4) and then *rises* by an extra 90° over the next two decades. The effect is shown in Figure 12.19.

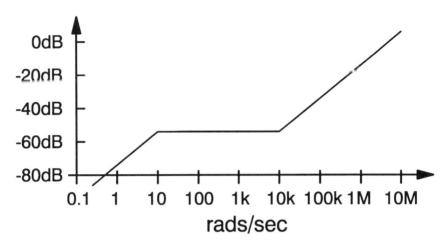

Figure 12.18: Amplitude Plot for $G_1 * G_2 * G_3 * G_4$.

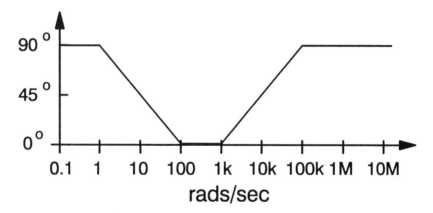

Figure 12.19: Phase Bode Plot for $G_1 * G_2 * G_3 * G_4$.

The last part to include is G_5. This is a conventional lowpass response so it stays at 0dB until its cutoff (10^7 rads/sec in this case) and then falls at 20dB decade. In this case the fall cancels the rise already present due to the effects of $G_{1\,to\,4}$. The overall, final effect is as shown in Figure 12.20.

The phase plot is identical to $G_{1\,to\,4}$ up to 10^6 rads/sec (one tenth of the cutoff frequency of G_5) and then falls by an extra $90°$ over the next two decades. The effect is shown in Figure 12.21.

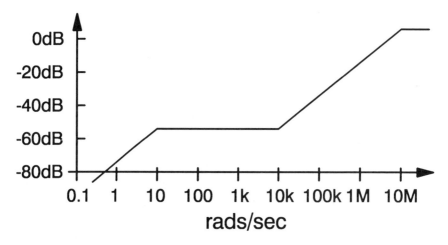

Figure 12.20: Amplitude Bode Plot for $G_{1\,to\,5}$, combined.

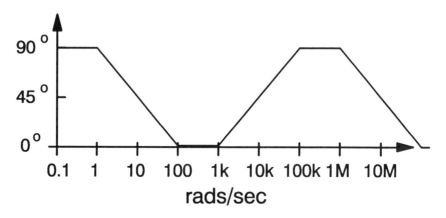

Figure 12.21: Phase Bode Plot for $G_{1\,to\,5}$, combined.

We now, finally, have the amplitude and phase responses for the complete transfer function. They are, of course, approximations as we are using straight line approximations to true Bode plots to build them up. However, they are quite good enough for most purposes and are a lot quicker to produce than programming a computer to do a true analysis. With practice, they can be sketched out by inspection.

There is one "complex" transfer function we should perhaps examine specifically and that is the high-pass response.

12.5 HIGH-PASS TRANSFER FUNCTION

This has the general form:-

$$\frac{v_{out}}{v_{in}} = K\frac{j\omega\tau}{1 + j\omega\tau}$$

Let us first assume that $K = 1$. As before, we split the transfer function into its individual parts. We have:-

$$\frac{v_{out}}{v_{in}} = \left[j\omega\tau\right]\left[\frac{1}{1 + j\omega\tau}\right]$$

The amplitude response of the first part is a straight line, rising at 20dB/decade. At a frequency $\omega = 1/\tau$ it passes through 0dB. The phase is a constant $+90°$. The amplitude and phase responses are shown as solid lines in Figures 12.22 and 12.23, respectively.

The amplitude response of the second part is a conventional low-pass response with cutoff at $\omega = 1/\tau$. The amplitude and phase responses are shown as dotted lines in Figure 12.22 and 12.23, respectively.

These two responses combine to give the amplitude and phase responses shown in Figures 12.24 and 12.25, respectively. This is the response of a true *high-pass* filter.

If the constant K in the original equation was not equal to one, this would have the effect of adding a constant value of $20\log_{10}(K)$ to the amplitude response. The phase response would be unchanged.

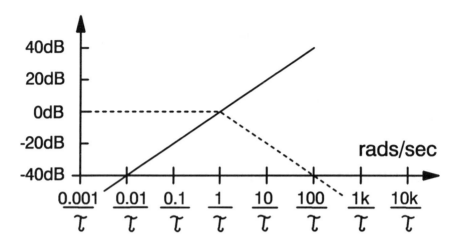

Figure 12.22: Amplitude Bode Plots for $j\omega$ (solid) and $1/(1 + j\omega\tau)$ (dotted)

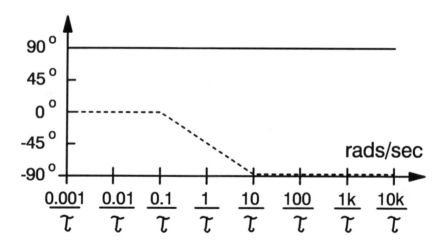

Figure 12.23: Phase Bode Plots for $j\omega$ (solid) and $1/(1 + j\omega\tau)$ (dotted)

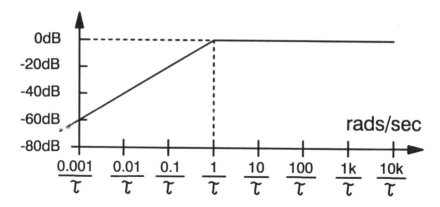

Figure 12.24: Amplitude Plot for $G(\omega) = j\omega\tau/(1 + j\omega\tau)$, a high-pass function.

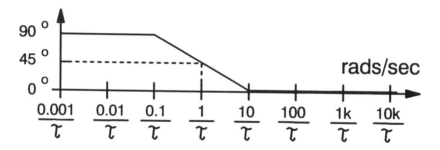

Figure 12.25: Phase Bode Plot for $G(\omega) = j\omega\tau/(1 + j\omega\tau)$, a high-pass function.

QUESTION

12.1) An amplifier has $\dfrac{v_{out}}{v_{in}} = \dfrac{10^5 \, (5 + j\omega)}{(100 + j\omega)(5000 + j\omega)}$

Draw the amplitude Bode plot and from it estimate the maximum voltage gain in dB. At what frequency is the voltage gain unity? Draw the Bode plot for the phase response of the amplifier.

$v_{in}(t)$ is set to $\sin(6000t)$. Using Bode plots find the amplitude and phase of v_{out}.

Chapter 13

DESIGN OF TRANSISTOR AMPLIFIERS
USING BODE PLOTS

Transistor amplifiers are generally *AC coupled*, that is they are connected to the surrounding circuitry through capacitors. This allows their DC bias conditions to be set independently from the circuits driving them or being driven by them. However, these capacitors have another effect; they introduce frequency sensitivity to the circuit. Consider the simple common emitter amplifier shown in Figure 13.1.

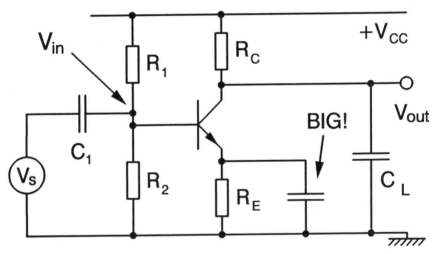

Figure 13.1: AC Coupled Common Emitter Transistor Amplifier

Notice that the input signal comes from v_s through capacitor C_1 and into the amplifier.

At first we will assume that the amplifier output is open circuit so at first sight it would appear that there is no load capacitance. However, associated with *every* transistor is a parasitic capacitor from collector to emitter. In the particular circuit under consideration this capacitance, C_L, is connected from the amplifier output to AC ground.

Now we know that the transistor amplifier has an input impedance and that in this case $R_{in} \approx R_1 \parallel R_2 \parallel h_{ie}$. Also the amplifier has an output impedance, R_{out}, which in this case is approximately equal to R_C.

The gain of this transistor amplifier was found some way back (page 60 or so) to be:-

$$\frac{v_{out}}{v_{in}} = \frac{-h_{fe} R_C}{h_{ie} + R_C h_{oe} h_{ie} - h_{fe} R_C h_{re}}$$

All this detail is a bit tedious so let's assume $h_{re} = 0$ and $h_{oe} = 0$. Further, we should include the effect of R_1 and R_2 so we should replace h_{ie} with R_{in} as defined above. This gives the gain as:-

$$A_v = \frac{v_{out}}{v_{in}} \approx \frac{-R_C}{R_{in}} h_{fe} = \frac{-R_C}{R_{in}} \beta$$

We can therefore replace the transistor amplifier with the simple model shown in Figure 13.2.

In this model the amplifier has been replaced by three elements; its input resistance R_{in}, its output resistance R_{out} and a "gain triangle" with A_v marked in it.

We can now see that the circuit has an input circuit (C_1 and R_{in}) and an output circuit (R_{out} and C_L) which are both frequency sensitive. The "gain triangle" is not frequency sensitive in itself; it provides the gain marked at all frequencies.

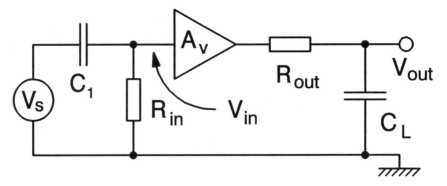

Figure 13.2: Model of AC Coupled Common Emitter Transistor Amplifier

13.1 THE INPUT CIRCUIT

The input circuit is C_1 and R_{in} as shown in Figure 13.3.

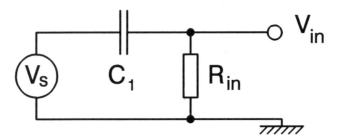

Figure 13.3: Input Circuit for AC Coupled Common Emitter Amplifier

This is a potential divider so:-

$$\frac{v_{out}}{v_{in}} = \frac{R_{in}}{R_{in} + X_c} = \frac{R_{in}}{R_{in} + 1/(j\omega C_1)} = \frac{R_{in}j\omega C_1}{R_{in}j\omega C_1 + 1}$$

This is the standard high pass function discussed on page 139 with $\tau = R_{in}C_1$. It has a cutoff frequency of $1/\tau$ rads/sec and a passband gain of 0dB.

If we pick normal values for the parameters, say $R_{in} = 800\Omega$ and $C_1 = 10\mu F$, the cutoff becomes 125 rads/sec or 20Hz. The amplitude and phase responses are shown as the solid lines in Figures 13.4 and 13.5, respectively.

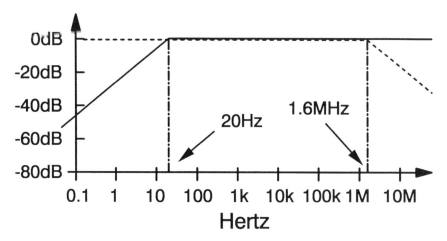

Figure 13.4: Amplitude responses of Input Circuit (solid)
and Output Circuit (dotted)

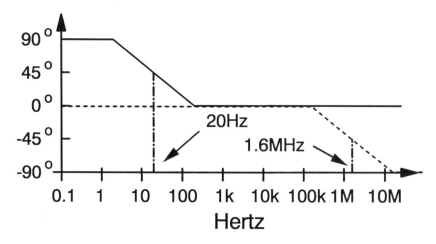

Figure 13.5: Phase responses of Input Circuit (solid) and Output Circuit (dotted)

13.2 THE OUTPUT CIRCUIT

The input circuit is C_L and R_{out} as shown in Figure 13.6.

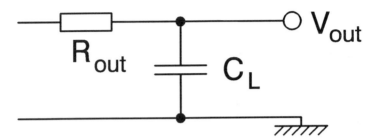

Figure 13.6: Output Circuit for AC Coupled Common Emitter Amplifier

Again this is a potential divider so:-

$$\frac{v_{out}}{v_{in}} = \frac{X_C}{R_{out} + X_C} = \frac{1/(j\omega C_L)}{R_{out} + 1/(j\omega C_L)} = \frac{1}{R_{out}j\omega C_L + 1}$$

This is the standard low pass function with $\tau = R_{out}C_L$. It has a cutoff frequency of $1/\tau$ rads/sec and a passband gain of 0dB.

If we pick fairly normal values for these parameters, say $R_{in} = 10\mathrm{k}\Omega$ and $C_L = 10\mathrm{pF}$ the cutoff becomes 10^7 rads/sec or 1.6MHz. The amplitude and phase responses are shown as the dotted lines in Figures 13.4 and 13.5, respectively. This theoretical cutoff frequency is good and high but in practice it would be rather lower because of the effects of wiring capacitance and, possibly, by other limitations inherent to the transistor.

If we combine the input and output frequency responses we get the amplitude and phase Bode Plots shown in Figures 13.7 and 13.8, respectively.

Clearly this is a *band-pass* structure. Low frequencies are cut out by the effects of C_1 and the amplifier input resistance while high frequencies are cut out by the effect of the amplifier output resistance and the capacitive load.

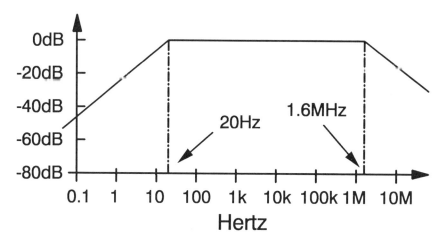

Figure 13.7: Amplitude Bode Plot of a Simple Transistor Amplifier

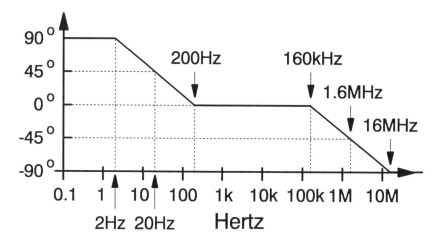

Figure 13.8: Phase Bode Plot of a Simple Transistor Amplifier

13.3 DESIGN EXAMPLE FOR COMMON EMITTER AMPLIFIER

We need an amplifier meeting the following specifications:-

Gain -5
Quiescent Power Consumption < 15mW

A 15V power supply is available. The circuit is to be driven from a voltage source through a 1μF decoupling capacitor and is to drive a purely capacitive load of 1000pF. Find the input and output impedances of the circuit you have designed, the passband width and gain.

The available transistor has $\beta = 100$, $h_{ie} = 800\Omega$ and $V_{CE(sat)} = 0.3$V.

SOLUTION (one of many!)

Power consumption is 15mW and power supply voltage is 15V. Therefore the quiescent current is 1mA. To bias the transistor for maximum possible output voltage swing we set the quiescent current at half the transistor "full ON" current so $I_{C(max)} = 2$mA. The maximum transistor current happens when the transistor is full ON, i.e. has 0.3V across it. Then the voltage across R_C and R_E is $15 - 0.3 = 14.7$V. The current through them is 2mA so $R_C + R_E = 14.7/2\,k\Omega = 7.35k\Omega$.

The gain is to be five. Thus $R_C/R_E = 5$. Combining with the above gives $R_E = 1.225k\Omega$ and $R_C = 6.125k\Omega$.

These values may be correct but finding those resistors in the stores will be tricky. These values give exactly 15mW power consumption. If we *increase* the values the power consumption will *decrease*. The next highest standard value for R_E is 1.5kΩ. Then $R_C = 5\,R_E = 7.5$kΩ, another standard value. (Extraordinary coincidence!) Take these values for our amplifier. The maximum current will be $14.7/(1.5 + 7.5)$mA $= 1.63$mA giving a quiescent power dissipation of 12.25mW, within spec.

The quiescent collector current will be 0.817mA giving a voltage on the emitter of 1.225V. The base voltage must be 0.7V higher than this so $V_B = 1.925$V.

Take R_2 to be 10kΩ (a nice value, standard and about ten times higher than R_E). Then by an amazing, unintentional, coincidence R_1 comes to 68kΩ.

Had accurate calculation led to a value for R_1 which was between two standard values, we would pick the *lower* standard value. This would tend to lift V_B above the optimum value. However, base current, which we have so far ignored, would tend to pull V_B down a bit. By choosing the lower standard value for R_1 we will have errors which *tend* to cancel.

Input impedance is given by:− $R_{in} = R_1 \| R_2 \| [h_{ie} + R_E(\beta + 1)]$

$$= 68k\Omega \| 10k\Omega \| [800\Omega + 1.5k\Omega(100 + 1)] = 8.246k\Omega$$

Note how the value for the input impedance is dominated by the bias chain.

Output impedance is equal to R_C and so is 7.5kΩ.

The lower cutoff frequency is given by the input decoupling capacitor (1μF) and R_{in}.

$$\text{Cutoff (rads/sec)} = 1/(R_{in} C_1) = 1/(8.246 * 10^3 * 1 * 10^{-6})$$

$$= 121.2 \text{ rads/sec} = 19.3\text{Hz}$$

The upper cutoff frequency is given by the load capacitor (1000pF) and R_{out}.

$$\text{Cutoff (rads/sec)} = 1/(R_{out} C_L) = 1/(7.5 * 10^3 * 1000 * 10^{-12})$$

$$= 1.33 * 10^5 \text{ rads/sec} = 21.22\text{kHz}$$

The passband width is therefore 21.22kHz − 19.3Hz = 21.2kHz. The passband gain is designed to be five *so long as the circuit is not loaded*. We will see what this means later.

13.4 EXAMPLE OF A CASCADED TRANSISTOR
AMPLIFIER

A student is required to design an amplifier with a DC gain of about 28.5dB and a passband to 5MHz. It will be driven by a voltage source with a negligibly low output impedance and will drive an extremely high impedance load. He has available transistors which have $\beta = 100$, $h_{ie} = 800\Omega$ and $V_{CE(sat)} = 0.3V$.

Q: What is the minimum permissible gain of the desired amplifier at DC and at 5MHz expressed as a voltage transfer ratio (not in dB)?

Ans: At DC we expect 28.5dB gain so in linear terms the gain must be $10^{28.5/20} \approx 26.6$. At 5MHz (the passband edge) the gain can be 3dB down on the DC value so the gain could be as low as $10^{25.5/20} \approx 18.8$

A student has already built two simple transistor amplifiers, the first with a linear gain of −6.8 and the second with a linear gain of −3.9. He has calculated and built them with the following resistor values:-

	Amplifier 1	Amplifier 2
Gain	−6	−4
R_C	6.8kΩ	3.9kΩ
R_E	1kΩ	1kΩ
R_1	82kΩ	56kΩ
R_2	10kΩ	10kΩ

Because of the method of construction, each amplifier has an input capacitance of 50pF.

Q: What is the input impedance of each of these amplifiers?

Ans: The input impedance is given by:-

$$R_{in} = R_1 \parallel R_2 \parallel [h_{ie} + (\beta + 1)R_E]$$

For both amplifiers the last term in this equation is equal to $800\Omega + 101 * 1k\Omega = 101.8k\Omega$. For the first amplifier $R_{in(1)} = 8.2k\Omega$ and for the second amplifier $R_{in(2)} = 7.832k\Omega$.

The student decides to make the desired amplifier system by cascading these two. He couples them together with great big capacitors which can be regarded as short circuits to AC at the frequencies of interest.

Q: What is the actual gain (linear) of the system at DC?

Ans: The gain of the first and second amplifiers at DC are 6.8 and 3.9, respectively. *However, the input impedance of the second amplifier loads down the first amplifier so the combined gain is not the product of the two individual gains.* The situation is as shown in Figure 13.9. For the moment, ignore the 50pF capacitors.

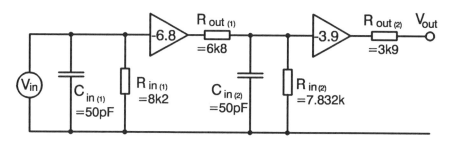

Figure 13.9: Model of two Cascaded Amplifiers

The gain is reduced by the two resistors $R_{out(1)}$ and $R_{in(2)}$ acting as a potential divider. This potential divider gives an attenuation of:-

$$\frac{v_{out}}{v_{in}} = \frac{7.832}{6.8 + 7.832} = 0.535$$

Therefore the gain at DC is $6.8 * 0.535 * 3.9 = 14.2$ instead of the 26.6 required.

Q: **What is the bandwidth of the system (MHz)?**

Ans: Looking at the model and including the effect of the capacitors we see the following.

(a)   The 50pF capacitor on the input of the first amplifier and the input resistance of the first amplifier do not matter because they are being driven by a voltage source.

(b)   The output resistance of the second amplifier does not matter because no output current is being drawn.

(c)   The centre block ($R_{out(1)}$, $C_{in}(2)$ and $R_{in(2)}$) make up a lowpass filter circuit which will limit the bandwidth of the system. Applying Kirchoffs Current Law to the input node of the second amplifier we have:-

$$\frac{v_{out(1)} - v_{in(2)}}{R_{out(1)}} = v_{in(2)}(j\omega C + 1/R_{in(2)})$$

With some rearrangement this gives:-

$$\frac{v_{in(2)}}{v_{out(1)}} = \frac{R_{in(2)}}{R_{in(2)} + R_{out(1)}} \left[\frac{1}{1 + \dfrac{R_{in(2)} R_{out(1)}}{R_{in(2)} + R_{out(1)}} j\omega C} \right]$$

This is a standard low pass transfer function with cutoff at $(R_{in(2)} + R_{out(1)})/(C R_{in(2)} R_{out(1)})$.

Substituting values gives the cutoff in rads/sec to be $5.5 * 10^6$ rads/sec or 874.5kHz.

Q: **What is the system gain at 5MHz (linear)?**

Ans: Because the cutoff frequency is 874.5kHz, the transfer function at 5MHz (5000kHz) must be:-

$$\frac{V_{out}}{V_{in}} = (DC\ gain) * \frac{1}{1 + j5000/874.5}$$

This has a magnitude of 0.1723 times the DC gain which is 15dB *less* than that already low value.

At 5MHz the system gain will be about one tenth of that required in the system specification. This has happened despite the fact that the student could have built each amplifier, tested it and found that it gave the full gain over the full frequency range. Forgetting that one stage loads down the stage driving it is a very popular error, particularly in the laboratories.

Q: How might this simple system be augmented to make it work to the required specifications? Mention the major factors that would have to be considered when designing the extra circuitry.

Ans: To stop this fall off in system gain an emitter-follower (common-collector) stage should be placed between the two sections of the amplifier. This emitter-follower would not need a DC bias chain as it could obtain its DC bias from the first amplier output. Thus its input impedance would be high. Also its input capacitance and its output impedance would be low.

One other point to note is that the amplifiers are the wrong way round. The lower gain amplifier, having the lower output impedance, should come *first*. This would almost double the frequency response in this case.

It should be noted that achieving gain at medium numbers of MegaHertz does require some thought, particularly with regard to loading and constructional techniques.

QUESTIONS

13.1) A simple common emitter amplifier ($R_E = 0$) is AC coupled via a
       $1\mu F$ capacitor at the input. If the input resistance of the amplifier is
       $30k\Omega$ determine the low frequency cut off of the amplifier. The
       amplifier has a collector load (and so output resistance) of $1k\Omega$.

       The collector-emitter junction of the transistor is shunted by a parasitic
       capacitance of $0.33pF$. What is the high frequency cut off of the
       amplifier? What is the bandwidth? What is the mid-band voltage
       gain in dB if $h_{fe} = 100$? Sketch the Bode plot of the amplifier voltage
       transfer function.

13.2) A voltage amplifier of $1k\Omega$ input resistance and $5k\Omega$ output resistance
       has an open circuit voltage gain of 400. What is this gain in dB?

       If the amplifier is driven from a matched ($1k\Omega$) voltage source into a
       matched ($5k\Omega$) load resistance, what is the amplifier terminal voltage
       gain in dB? [46dB]

13.3) If the load resistance in question 13.2 is changed to $10k\Omega$ what is the
       terminal voltage gain in dB? Is the power developed in the $10k\Omega$ load
       greater or less than the example in question 13.2? If the load resistor
       is connected through a series (coupling) capacitor of $1\mu F$, does this
       form a high pass or low pass amplifier circuit? What is the $-3dB$ cut
       off frequency in Hz?

13.4) Figure 13.10 shows the circuit for a simple common emitter amplifier.

       The gain is to be -3.4, capacitor C_1 is so large that its impedance can
       be neglected, the transistor has $V_{CE(sat)} = 0.3V$ and the quiescent
       power dissipation is to be somewhere between 10mW and 15mW.
       Find suitable standard values for R_E and R_C.

       The amplifier is to be DC biased in such a manner that the output
       voltage swing is maximised. Noting that R_2 is to be $15k\Omega$, as shown,
       find the *exact* value for R_1 that will achieve this. Choose an
       appropriate standard value for R_1, stating why you have chosen it to
       be larger or smaller than the exact value.

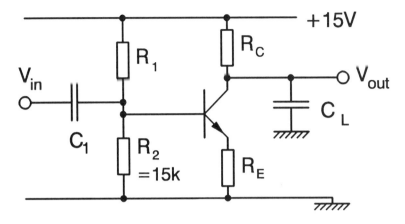

Figure 13.10: Simple Common Emitter Amplifier

Given that the passband of this amplifier is to extend to 500Hz, what is the maximum possible value of C_L?

13.5) Find V_o/V_{in} for the circuit in Figure 13.11.

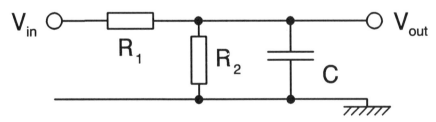

Figure 13.11: Simple R-C Circuit

What is the cutoff frequency, ω_o, in rad/sec in terms of R_1, R_2 and C?

Find $\left| \dfrac{V_o}{V_{in}} \right|$ for $\omega = K\omega_o$.

It is necessary to design an amplifier with a DC gain of at least 25dB and a passband to 5MHz. It will be driven by a voltage source with a negligibly low output impedance and will drive an extremely high impedance load.

What is the minimum permissible gain of the desired amplifier at DC and at 5MHz expressed as a voltage transfer ratio (not in dB)?

Available are two identical DC coupled amplifiers with the following characteristics:-

Gain	−5 (linear)
C_{in}	50pF
R_{in}	20kΩ
R_{out}	1kΩ

It is decided to make the desired amplifier system by cascading these two.

What is the actual gain (linear) of the system at DC? What is the bandwidth of the system (MHz)? What is the system gain at 5MHz (linear)?

How might this simple system be augmented to make it work to the required specifications?

13.6) The circuit of a simple common emitter amplifier stage is shown in Figure 13.12(a).

Draw the small-signal model of this amplifier including the bias resistors R_1 and R_2.

Assuming that β for the transistor is infinite and $h_{re} = h_{oe} = 0$, find the small-signal input impedance of the amplifier, R_{in}.

Now assume that the amplifier input is coupled through a 1μF capacitor to a voltage source, v_s, and its output is coupled directly to a capacitive load of 0.1μF. Also, $R_1 = 47kΩ$, $R_2 = 5.6kΩ$, $R_C = 1kΩ$ and $R_E = 500Ω$. This situation is shown in Figure 13.12(b). Assuming that this common emitter amplifier has an

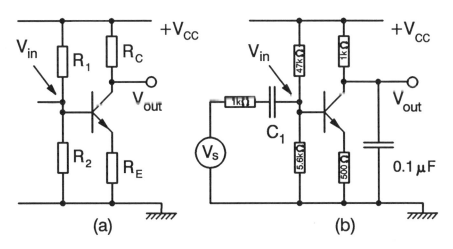

Figure 13.12: Simple Common Emitter Amplifier

output impedance of 1kΩ, find the transfer function v_{out}/v_s.

Draw the Bode Plots of the amplitude and phase responses of this amplifier.

Find from the graphs the gain and phase-shift in this complete amplifier at 3kHz.

Chapter 14

AMPLIFIER CLASSIFICATION

This is a bit of a sideline; it doesn't fit in. However, it should be said somewhere!

Amplifiers can be classed into four distinct types:-

1) **Voltage Amplifier**

   A voltage amplifier takes in a *voltage* signal and produces an output *voltage*. The gain is a number without units.

2) **Current Amplifier**

   A current amplifier takes in a *current* signal and produces an output *current*. The gain is a number without units.

3) **Transresistance Amplifier**

   A transresistance amplifier takes in a *current* signal and produces an output *voltage*. The gain is V_{out}/I_{in} and is in *OHMS*.

4) **Transconductance Amplifier**

   A transconductance amplifier takes in a *voltage* signal and produces an output *current*. The gain is I_{out}/V_{in} and is in *SIEMENS* (which used to be called MHOs).

Chapter 15

OPERATIONAL AMPLIFIERS

An operational amplifier (**op-amp**) is a device which amplifies the difference between two signals by a very large value. Its inputs and outputs are *voltages*.

An op-amp has two inputs, the *inverting input* and the *non-inverting input*. If the voltage on the *inverting* input *rises* the op-amp output *falls*. If the voltage on the *non-inverting* input *rises* the op-amp output *rises*.

The op-amp takes the *difference* between the two inputs, amplifies it by a *large* number and produces the result as an output voltage. Therefore the equation for a op-amp is:-

$$V_{out} = A\,(V_{in(non-inverting)} - V_{in(inverting)})$$

Where "A" is the gain and is large (10^5?).

We will sometimes write the voltage on the inverting input as $V_{in(inverting)}$ and sometimes as V_{in-}. They are the same. Similarly for the voltage on the non-inverting input, $V_{in(non-inverting)}$ or V_{in+}.

A typical op-amp is made up of a collection of bipolar transistors arranged as a *differential* stage, a *gain* stage and an *output* stage. Sometimes field effect devices are used instead of bipolar devices but they have intrinsically lower gain and so tend to be used only for the input stage (to reduce input current).

The circuit diagram of a very simple, old-fashioned op-amp is shown in Figure 15.1.

This op-amp can be seen to be old-fashioned because it is simple (!) and it uses lots of resistors which take up huge areas on the silicon chip. It also requires plus and minus power supplies and a ground connection.

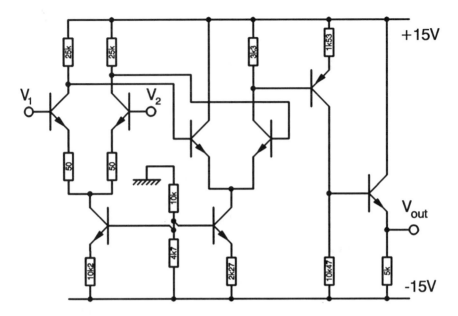

Figure 15.1: Circuit Diagram of Old-fashioned Op-amp.

The circuit diagram for an op-amp which is probably the most widely used of all, the 741, is given in Figure 15.2.

As you can see, the circuit is becoming a little more complex. Modern op-amps are even more complicated and perform very much better than this simple 741.

In a little book like this we cannot attempt to analyse these circuits. In this chapter we will consider the op-amp as a "black box" which behaves in a certain manner.

The behaviour of an ideal op-amp and a real op-amp (741C) are as summarised in the following table.

Parameter	Ideal Value	Practical Value (Typical 741C)
Gain	Infinite	$2 * 10^5 = 106dB$
Input Current	Zero	80nA
Bandwidth	Infinite	0dB Gain (Open Loop) at 1MHz
Output Voltage Range	Unlimited	Power Supplies minus 2V
Output Impedance	Zero	75Ω
Power Consumption	Zero	50mW
Slew Rate	Infinite	0.5V/μs
Common Mode Rejection Ratio	Infinite	90dB
Power Supply Rejection Ratio	Zero	30μV/V
Input Offset Voltage	Zero	2mV

This is a fairly full set of parameters (but not complete) and not all will be important to us. The first five are the ones we will spend time on. However, let us consider all these parameters in turn.

15.1 GAIN

The gain is the open-loop gain of the op-amp, given as the parameter "A" in the equation. The open-loop gain is the gain *without any feedback*. We would like "A" to be infinite but that is impossible so we settle for "A" having a very large value. We would hope for $A > 10^5 = 100dB$ and this is easily achieved *at low frequencies* in most stand-alone op-amps. In some small op-amps, however, particularly in analogue chips where some tens of op-amps are used in one IC design, the gain made be traded-off against size in which case "A" may only be a little over 100.

15.2 INPUT CURRENT

We do not want any current to flow into the input terminals of the op-amp. This requirement is fairly easily approximated if MOSFET input devices are used in which case the input resistance can be of the order of $10^{12}\Omega$. When bipolar input transistors are used input resistances will be a lot smaller but should still be greater than about 1MΩ.

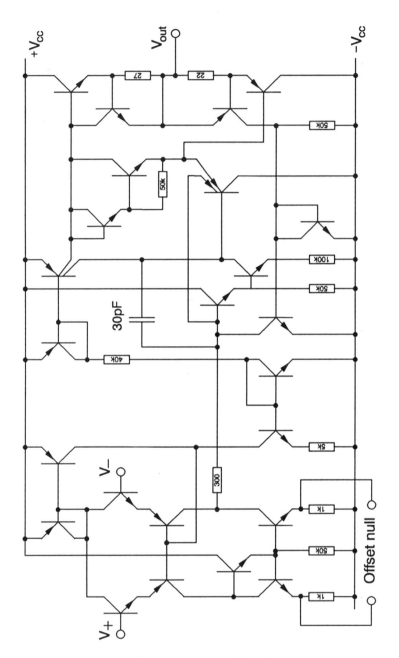

Figure 15.2: Circuit Diagram of 741 Op-amp.

15.3 BANDWIDTH

An ideal op-amp would work at any frequency, DC→∞. Unfortunately it is fairly safe to say that a 741 will not work at 1GHz so we can see that real op-amps cannot meet this requirement. In fact, a 741 can only achieve its full open-loop gain up to 10Hz. After 10Hz the gain falls off at 20dB/decade. (Familiar value?)

The Bode Plot of op-amp gain will be like that shown in Figure 15.3 (which is for a 741).

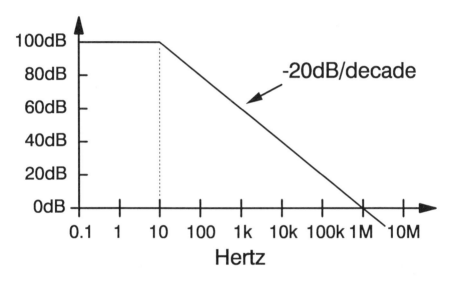

Figure 15.3: Bode Plot for Gain of 741

You will see that this is a first order lowpass response. For reasons we will examine later, the response is *tailored* by the op-amp designer to be of this form.

15.4 OUTPUT VOLTAGE RANGE

If we take the simple equation $V_{out} = A(V_{in+} - V_{in-})$ and we connect a 12V car battery (my favourite voltage source) across the inputs we get:-

$$V_{out} = A(12V) = 1.2MV$$

using the value for "A" for a 741 (10^5). This result is a bit silly. We are just not going to get over a MegaVolt out of a cheap, nasty, IC like a 741. So what happened?

The output voltage range of an op-amp is always limited, at least by the power supply voltages from which it is running. Therefore, if we are using $\pm 15V$ power supplies, we cannot expect the op-amp output to go outside the range $-15V$ to $+15V$. In fact, in the 741, the output voltage swing is not even that good; it tends to be about 2V less than the power supply. Thus, for a 741 running from $\pm 15V$ power supplies the output voltage range would be about $\pm 13V$.

If the equation $V_{out} = A(V_{in+} - V_{in-})$ produces a value outside the permissible range the op-amp output *saturates* at either its minimum or maximum value. I often say the op-amp is "not behaving" when this happens.

Op-amps are often used in such a manner that their outputs are almost always smashed against either the upper or lower output limits. In this case the output can be considered a *digital* value and the op-amp is called a *comparator*.

15.5 OUTPUT IMPEDANCE

We would like the output of an op-amp to be like a voltage source, i.e. to have zero output impedance. This cannot be achieved but with real output impedances of less than 100Ω we are usually close enough if the external circuit is designed with a little thought.

15.6 POWER CONSUMPTION

Engineers would always like circuits to work without consuming power. Sadly, life ain't like that and op-amps do take power. However op-amps which consume only a few μW are available though there is always a trade-off against speed, slew rate, and all the other goodies we would like to have.

15.7 SLEW RATE

An op-amp output voltage cannot change instantaneously even if its input should, somehow, change instantaneously. The maximum possible rate of change of its output voltage is called the *slew rate* and is usually given in volts per microsecond. The 741 manages about 0.5V/μs but other op-amps are better. Values of 20V/μs are pretty good.

Note that slew rate is a *large signal* phenomenon. It is, in some ways, related to bandwidth but it is certainly not an obvious relationship.

15.8 COMMON MODE REJECTION RATIO (CMRR)

Op-amps are meant to amplify the *difference* between their two inputs. Therefore, if we connect the two inputs together and to a signal we should get no signal at the output. Unfortunately, this being real life, we do. The signal "gain" from input to output when connected this way is the *common-mode* gain, A_{CM}. It should be *much* less than one (much less output than input).

The desirable gain is the amount *difference mode* signals are amplified, "A" in the equations, often written A_{DM}.

The ratio A_{DM}/A_{CM}, converted to dB is called the *common mode rejection ratio* or CMRR.

Thus:$-$ $$CMRR = 20\log_{10}(A_{DM}/A_{CM})$$

15.9 POWER SUPPLY REJECTION RATIO (PSRR)

The power supply rejection ratio (PSRR) is similar in its definition to the CMRR, discussed above. It is a measure of how the op-amp output varies as the power supply voltage varies. Therefore, if the PSRR is given ia $30\mu V/V$, a one volt ripple (variation) of the op-amp power supply voltage would result in a $30\mu V$ variation in the op-amp output signal.

15.10 INPUT OFFSET VOLTAGE

If the two input terminals of an op-amp are tied together the op-amp output should be zero. Once again, life ain't like that. Usually, because of imbalances inside the op-amp, the op-amp output will be saturated.

The *input offset voltage* is that voltage which when applied *between* the two input terminals results in a zero output voltage. Obviously, we would like this voltage to be very small. Good instrumentation op-amps will reduce this value to small numbers of μV and chopper stabilisation will reduce it further. FET input op-amps tend to be worse than bipolar op-amps in this respect.

15.11 TECHNIQUES FOR OP-AMP CIRCUIT ANALYSIS

When analysing an op-amp circuit we nearly always assume that the op-amp behaves in an ideal manner. In particular, we usually assume that it has infinite gain, no input current and no problems in operating at the frequencies we want.

The assumption that it has infinite gain has a very useful corollary. *Assume first that the op-amp is "behaving"*, i.e. that its output is not saturated. Then the output voltage, V_{out}, is a fairly small number (limited by the power supply voltages). Because we have made this assumption the usual equation:-

$$V_{out} = A\left(V_{in(non-inverting)} - V_{in(inverting)}\right)$$

is true. We can turn this equation round in an obvious manner to get:-

$$\left(V_{in(non-inverting)} - V_{in(inverting)}\right) = V_{out}/A$$

Since V_{out} is moderate and "A" is very large indeed, we can see that $(V_{in(non-inverting)} - V_{in(inverting)})$ must be very small. In fact, we usually assume that it is so small that:-

$$V_{in(non-inverting)} = V_{in(inverting)}$$

Note that this does not hold if the op-amp output is saturated. (An op-amp is *saturated* if its output is as high as possible or as low as possible, limited by the available power supply voltages.)

Chapter 16

SIMPLE OP-AMP CIRCUITS

All practical op-amp circuits use *feedback*. That is to say, some of the output is taken and fed back to the input. Usually we use *negative feedback*. When the feedback is negative it is organised so that a rise (say) in the op-amp output will be fed back to the op-amp input in such a manner that the rise is, to some extent, cancelled.

Negative feedback always reduces the system gain to a value *less* than the open-loop gain of the op-amp.

16.1 NON-INVERTING GAIN CIRCUIT

Consider the circuit shown in Figure 16.1.

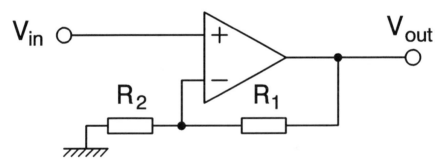

Figure 16.1: Non-Inverting Op-amp Circuit

In this circuit a fraction of the output voltage ($R_2/[R_1 + R_2]$) is fed back to the op-amp inverting input.

Because the op-amp inputs take no current (or at least, so little that we don't worry about it) we can say:-

$$V_{in(inverting)} = \frac{R_2}{R_1 + R_2} V_{out}$$

Now we have that $V_{in(inverting)} = V_{in(non-inverting)} = V_{in}$

Therefore:— $V_{in} = \dfrac{R_2}{R_1 + R_2} V_{out} \Rightarrow \dfrac{V_{out}}{v_{in}} = \dfrac{R_1 + R_2}{R_2}$

Note that the gain is determined by a ratio of resistors, *not* by the gain of the op-amp itself.

16.2 VOLTAGE FOLLOWER

Consider the circuit shown in Figure 16.2.

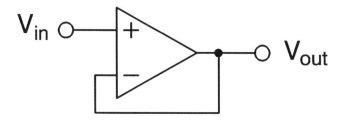

Figure 16.2: Voltage Follower Circuit

In this circuit the output voltage is equal to the inverting input voltage (they are connected). Also the inverting input voltage is equal to the non-inverting input voltage (op-amps are like that) which is equal to the input. Thus, in this circuit, the input and output voltages are equal. This is a *voltage follower* circuit with a gain of one.

The voltage follower is used as a buffer amplifier because it has a very high input impedance (the input impedance of the op-amp) and a very low output impedance (the output impedance of the op-amp).

16.3 INVERTING AMPLIFIER

The basic inverting op-amp amplifier is shown in Figure 16.3.

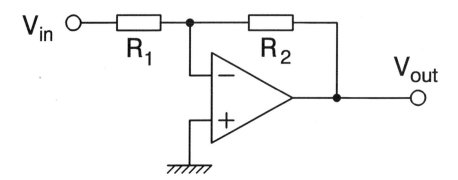

Figure 16.3: Inverting Amplifier

To analyse this circuit we apply Kirchoff's current law to the inverting input.

We have:−
$$\frac{V_{out} - V_{in-}}{R_2} + \frac{V_{in} - V_{in-}}{R_1} = 0$$

We note that since $V_{in-} = V_{in+}$ and $V_{in+} = 0$ then $V_{in-} = 0$. Combining this observation with the above equation and rearranging gives:-

$$\frac{V_{out}}{V_{in}} = \frac{-R_2}{R_1}$$

16.4 DIFFERENCE AMPLIFIER

The circuit shown in Figure 16.4 takes the difference between two input signals and amplifies it by a value set by a resistor ratio.

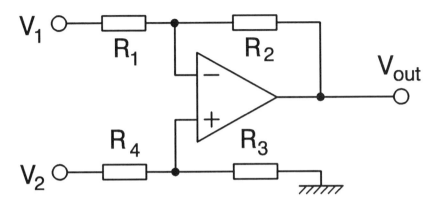

Figure 16.4: Op-amp Difference Amplifier

We analyse the circuit by writing down Kirchoff's current laws applied to each of the two op-amp inputs.

$$\frac{V_1 - V_{in-}}{R_1} + \frac{V_{out} - V_{in-}}{R_2} = 0 \quad \text{and} \quad \frac{V_2 - V_{in+}}{R_4} = \frac{V_{in+}}{R_3}$$

Remembering that $V_{in+} = V_{in-}$ we combine these to obtain:-

$$V_{out} = V_2 \frac{R_3(R_1 + R_2)}{R_1(R_3 + R_4)} - V_1 \frac{R_2}{R_1}$$

If we then pick resistor values so that:- $\quad \dfrac{R_4}{R_3} = \dfrac{R_1}{R_2}$

we will get:- $\quad V_{out} = R_2/R_1 \, (V_2 - V_1)$

Note that this only works if we get the resistor values *absolutely* right. In practice, when we use normal resistors from the stores (5%?) the inevitable resistor inaccuracies lead to this circuit working rather poorly.

QUESTIONS

16.1) Derive an expression for the output voltage, V_o, of the amplifier
       shown in Figure 16.5 in terms of the three inputs. You may assume
       that the operational amplifier is ideal and has an open loop gain which
       is independent of frequency.

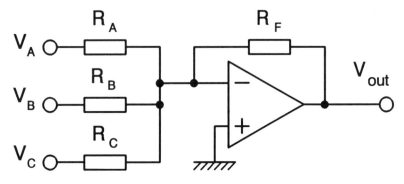

Figure 16.5: Op-Amp Circuit

16.2) What type of filter circuit is shown in Figure 16.6? Determine the DC
       voltage gain and the 3dB cut off frequency. You may assume that the
       operational amplifier is ideal and has an open loop gain which is
       independent of frequency. What is the voltage gain and phase shift at
       half and twice this frequency?

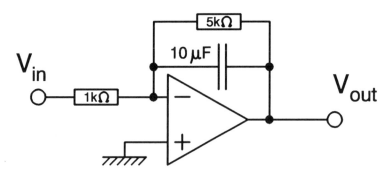

Figure 16.6: Op-Amp Filter Circuit

Chapter 17

STABILITY OF A SYSTEM WITH FEEDBACK

Op-amps are almost always used with negative feedback. When this is not the case they are almost certainly being used as oscillators or comparators. The block diagram of a system with negative feedback is shown in Figure 17.1.

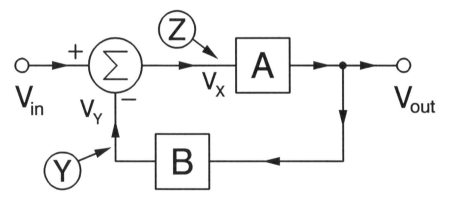

Figure 17.1: System with Negative Feedback

The input signal is V_{in}. From it is subtracted the output of the feedback network, V_f, giving the input to the amplifier, V_x. The amplifier has gain "A" so its output is $A V_x = V_{out}$. V_{out} is multiplied by "B", the gain of the feedback network, to give $V_f = B V_{out}$. We therefore have:-

$$V_{out} = A(V_{in} - B V_{out}) \Rightarrow \frac{V_{out}}{V_{in}} = \frac{A}{1 + AB}$$

Note that as B tends to zero (no feedback) this gives $V_{out}/V_{in} = A$, as expected.

Also, as A tends to infinity the equation implies that V_{out}/V_{in} tends to 1/B.

17.1 LOOP GAIN

A very important concept here is that of *loop gain*. The loop gain is the gain from point Z on Figure 17.1 (the input of the amplifier) through the amplifier and through the feedback network to point Y, the output of the feedback network. The appropriate equation is very simple:-

$$\text{Loop Gain} = A\,B$$

If there is no phase shift through the amplifier or the feedback network the magnitude of the loop gain will be AB.

The feedback networks we will normally be using will be purely resistive so there will be no phase shift in the feedback network. However, the amplifier is an op-amp which has a frequency response so there will be a phase shift through the amplifier.

17.2 SYSTEM STABILITY

Let us suppose that there was a phase shift of exactly $-180°$ through the op-amp. Then, round the whole loop (subtractor included), there would be a phase shift of 180° due to the subtractor and $-180°$ due to the op-amp. Thus there would be no overall phase shift round the loop. The effect would be that what looked like negative feedback would become positive feedback.

Suppose there was a small signal present at point Z (possibly a small noise pulse) and that this signal was at exactly that frequency at which there was $-180°$ phase shift through the op-amp. That signal would travel round the loop and be multiplied in amplitude by $|AB|$. Its phase would not change. It would then go round the loop again and would be multiplied by $|AB|$ again, so giving a gain of $|AB|^2$. This process would continue till after, say, 100 spins round the loop the signal had been multiplied by $|AB|^{100}$.

If $|AB|$ is even a tiny bit greater than one the signal will grow and grow until it is the biggest signal present on the system, totally swamping any input signal we may apply. The system output will totally comprise this growing, unwanted signal and the system is said to be *unstable*.

If |AB| is less than one the unwanted signal will decay away until it disappears and the system is said to be *stable*.

If |AB| is *exactly* equal to one our unwanted signal will remain at its original amplitude forever. This situation is most unlikely to occur unless we want it to happen and carefully design the system so that it will. We would then have an oscillator.

17.3 GAIN MARGIN

If we found the frequency, ω_0, at which the phase shift through the amplifier was exactly $-180°$ and calculated $A(\omega_0)B$ $(= |A(\omega_0)B|$ at this frequency) **and converted it to dB** the value would be negative if the system was stable and positive if unstable. The amount by which |AB| is less than 0dB at the $-180°$ phase shift frequency is called the *gain margin*. Being a "margin", like in "safety margin", positive values are good (stable system) and negative values are bad (unstable system). Thus:-

$$\text{Gain Margin} = -20\log_{10}|A(\omega_0)B|$$

where ω_0 is such that:-

$$\text{Arg}[A(\omega_0)B] = \text{Arg}[A(\omega_0)] = -180°$$

We could draw bode amplitude and phase plots of AB and we might end up with something like those shown in Figure 17.2.

The function AB shown must be a third order system because the maximum phase shift is $-270°$. We can see that at the frequency where the phase shift is $-180°$ the gain is about 15dB. This would be bad news if we wanted a stable system. The gain margin is -15dB so instability would result.

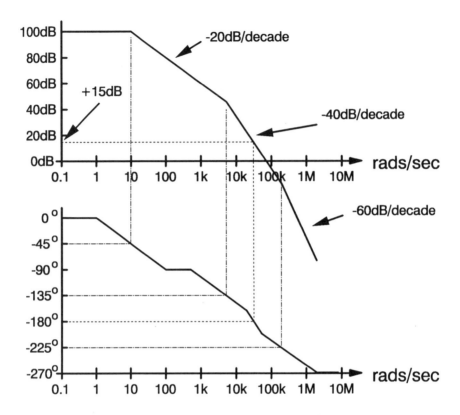

Figure 17.2: Bode Amplitude and Phase Plots of AB (third order system)

17.4 PHASE MARGIN

The other way of measuring stability is the *phase margin*. Using this technique we first find the frequency where the loop gain |AB| is 0dB and measure the phase shift *through the amplifier*†. This phase shift will start at 0° and become increasingly *negative*. We then measure the phase shift at the frequency where the loop gain is 0dB. The amount by which this phase shift is *greater than* −180° is the *phase margin*.

---

† The phase shift through the amplifier is Arg[A], not Arg[−AB] which is the phase shift through the *loop* including the sub-tractor.

$$\text{Phase Margin} = \text{Arg}[\, A(\omega_o)\, B] - (-180°) = \text{Arg}[\, A(\omega_o)\,] + 180°$$

where ω_o is such that:$-$ $20\log_{10} |A(\omega_o)\, B| = 0\text{dB}$

Suppose we have bode plots for AB as shown in Figure 17.3.

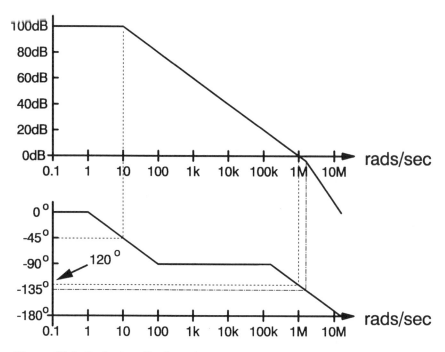

Figure 17.3: Bode Amplitude and Phase Plots of AB (second order system).

Here AB is a second order function because the maximum phase shift is $-180°$. We project the 0dB frequency down from the amplitude plot to the phase plot and see that in this case there is a phase margin of about 60° (phase shift through amplifier of $-120°$ and $[\, -120° - (-180°)\,] = 60°$).

17.5 STABILITY WITH VARYING AMOUNTS OF FEEDBACK

The important factor in determining system stability is the magnitude and phase of the loop gain. If we are using purely resistive feedback the phase of the loop gain will not vary as the amount of feedback is varied. In other words, phase does not vary with B. Therefore, the frequency at which the phase of the loop reaches $-180°$, ω_0, does not depend on B, only on A. "A" is the gain of the amplifier and so ω_0 depends only on the op-amp.

Clearly the magnitude of the loop gain, $|AB|$, does depend on the value of B. To maximise our gain margin we want the gain at ω_0 to be *minimised*.

Since the value of "A" at a given frequency is outside our control, maximum gain margin (i.e. maximum system stability) comes with *minimum* values of B.

Conversely, worst system stability comes with maximum values of "B". Because the *system* gain at high values of "A" is approximately 1/B worst case stability happens when the system gain is *least*.

For these reasons the most potentially unstable op-amp circuit is the simple voltage follower shown in Figure 16.2. Here the feedback is maximum (100%) so the loop gain is maximum and the gain margin is *minimum*.

Chapter 18

OP-AMP FREQUENCY RESPONSE

A typical op-amp comprises three parts. There is a *differential stage* which gives some gain but has as its main function the subtraction of V_{in+} and V_{in-}. Following the differential stage comes the *gain stage* which gives high gain but has a high output impedance. The last stage is a *output stage* which has a high input impedance and a low output impedance. This setup is shown in Figure 18.1.

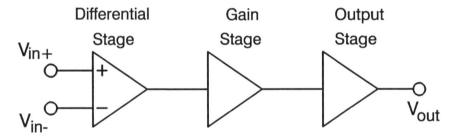

Figure 18.1: Block Diagram of Op-amp.

Each of the three stages in the op-amp has a frequency response and it can be shown that each is first-order low-pass. The cutoff frequency are usually different for each stage with the output stage having the highest and the other two being of the same order.

Using the techniques we developed earlier we can draw reasonable approximations to the amplitude and phase bode plots for each of these three stages. Clearly the actual values of cutoff, gain, etc. will depend on the actual circuit, component values, etc. The result is shown in Figure 18.2.

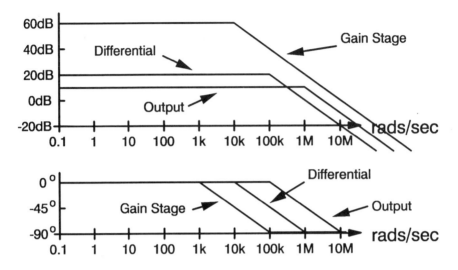

Figure 18.2: Bode Plots for the three Stages of an Op-amp

We can combine the three individual gain and phase plots as shown in Figure 18.3. (Ignore the chained lines at present).

The Gain and Phase margins are also drawn in Figure 18.3 (-50dB and -67.5°) and it can be seen that all is not well; both are negative. Therefore, if we were to actually make this op-amp it would be unstable; it would oscillate (or "hoot" or "sing"). This would happen as soon as feedback was applied; no input signal would be required.

This op-amp requires *compensation*. There are many subtle methods of compensating a system. The method we will examine next is the most crude but all methods involve supplying a "dominant pole". For the purposes of this course we will just say that this implies making the system have a response which is nearly first-order low-pass.

The coarse method involves connecting a simple R-C low-pass filter in series with the op-amp output as shown in Figure 18.4.

How do we find the cutoff frequency of this extra R-C filter?

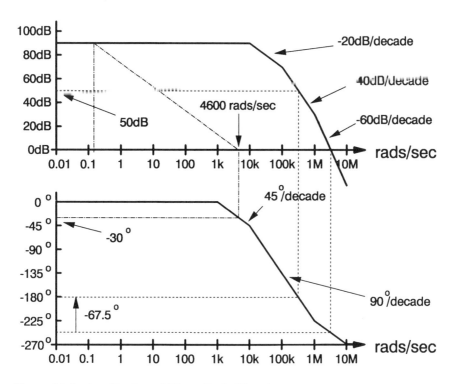

Figure 18.3: Amplitude and Phase Bode Plots for an Uncompensated Op-Amp

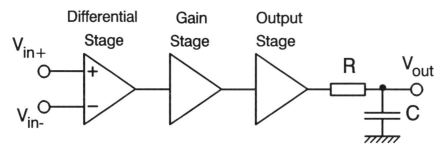

Figure 18.4: Op-Amp Block Diagram Including Primitive Compensation

First we must determine the desired phase margin. Let us assume here that we would like a phase margin of 60°. Then, at the frequency where the whole (fourth-order) system has a gain of 0dB, the total phase shift should be $-120°$ ($-180° - (-60°)$).

Let us assume that the three cutoff frequencies associated with the original third-order system are at "moderately high" frequencies. In the example given the lowest is at 10kHz. In nearly all realistic amplifiers of this type the low-frequency gains will be high and, experience suggests, this combination of circumstances will result in a requirement that the cut-off frequency of our extra R-C filter be low.

If this is, in fact, the case the phase shift of the R-C filter will all happen at low frequencies and, at medium frequencies, where we find the cutoff frequencies of the original third-order system the phase shift of the R-C filter will be $-90°$.

Therefore the phase shift associated with the original, third-order, system, at the frequency where the gain of the new, fourth-order, system is 0dB must be $-30°$ ($-120° - (-90°)$).

Examine the Phase Bode Plot for the uncompensated op-amp (the original third-order system) given in Figure 18.3 and find the frequency where the phase shift is $-30°$. From the chained lines in the graph we find that this is approximately 4600 rads/sec. At this frequency the gain of the compensated op-amp must have fallen to 0dB if it is to have a 60° phase margin.

The amplitude response of the uncompensated op-amp (Figure 18.3) is flat at 90dB from DC to 10000 rads/sec. Therefore the response up to 4600 rads/sec will be entirely dominated by our extra R-C filter. The response from DC to 4600 rads/sec will be exactly first-order. The graph must go through the points (0 rads/sec, 90dB) and (4600 rads/sec, 0dB). (As the graph is on a log frequency scale we cannot plot 0 rads/sec so we substitute a suitable low value.)

The graph is a first-order low-pass response so its downward sloping section must have a gradient of -20dB/decade.

Draw a line with a gradient of -20dB/decade through the point (4600 rads/sec, 0dB). Where this line intersects with the horizontal line representing a gain of 90dB will be the cutoff of the R-C filter. This operation is shown graphically using chained lines in Figure 18.5 and we find that the cutoff frequency of the R-C filter must be about 0.15 rads/sec.

We could also note that rising from 0dB to 90dB is 4½ blocks of 20dB and therefore the cutoff frequency must be 4½ decades less than 4600 rads/sec. We could then divide 4600 by antilog(4.5) to get 0.1454 rads/sec, the required cut-off frequency.

The amplitude and phase responses of the compensated op-amp are shown in Figure 18.5.

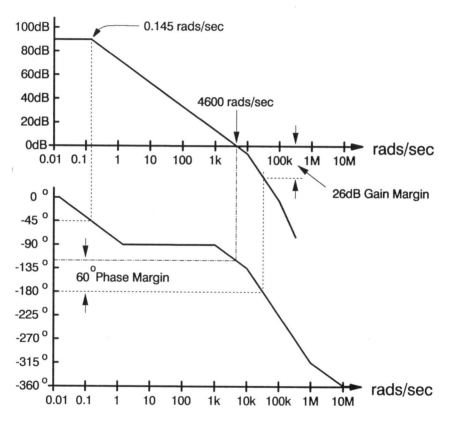

Figure 18.5: Response of Op-Amp with Simple Compensation

We can see that the gain and phase margins are now positive and a system built using this op-amp will be stable. However, the frequency response is now much worse than before. Still, it is usable now and it wasn't before. This is success.

Normal techniques of op-amp compensation involve "pole-splitting" which results in the op-amp having the same sort of first order response but not quite such a horribly low cutoff frequency. Remember that the cutoff frequency of the 741 is only 10Hz.

Since compensation is always required the frequency response of all op-amps is first-order low-pass, at least up to the frequency where the open-loop gain has fallen to unity (the "unity-gain" frequency). Therefore the transfer function of an op-amp can be fairly well approximated by:-

$$A_{ol}(\omega) = \frac{A_{ol}(DC)}{1 + j\omega/\omega_c}$$

where ω_c is the cutoff of the op-amp response in rads/sec ($2 * \pi * 10$ rads/sec for a 741) and ω is the frequency of interest in rads/sec.

Given the frequency ω_c we can find the unity gain bandwidth and vice versa. At the unity gain bandwidth frequency, ω_{ug}, $A_{ol}(\omega_{ug}) = 1$. Thus:-

$$A_{ol}(\omega_{ug}) = \frac{A_{ol}(DC)}{1 + j\omega_{ug}/\omega_c} = 1$$

Since ω_{ug} will be very high this implies:-

$$\omega_{ug} = A_{ol}(DC) * \omega_c$$

For a 741 and sticking to Hertz (as the 2π factors cancel) we have $f_c = 10Hz$ and $A_{ol}(DC) = 10^5$. These give the unity gain bandwidth as 1MHz, very close to the truth.

18.1 FREQUENCY RESPONSE OF OP-AMP WITH FEEDBACK

Consider the basic non-inverting amplifier shown in Figure 18.6.

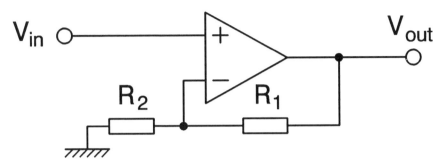

Figure 18.6: Non-Inverting Op-Amp Based Amplifier

The basic formulae are:— $V_{out} = A(V_{in+} - V_{in-})$ and

$$V_{in-} = V_{out} * R_2/(R_1 + R_2)$$

However, "A" is not now just a scalar, it is the transfer function:-

$$A_{ol}(\omega) = \frac{A_{ol}(DC)}{1 + j\omega/\omega_c} \quad \text{with} \quad \tau = 1/\omega_c$$

Combining these gives:-

$$V_{out}(\omega) = \frac{A_{ol}(DC)}{1 + j\omega\tau} \left[V_{in} - \frac{R_2}{R_1 + R_2} V_{out} \right]$$

$$\Rightarrow \frac{V_{out}}{V_{in}} = \frac{A_{ol}(DC)(R_1 + R_2)}{(1 + j\omega\tau)(R_1 + R_2) + A_{ol}(DC)R_2}$$

$$\Rightarrow \frac{V_{out}}{V_{in}} = \frac{R_1 + R_2}{R_2} \left[\frac{1}{1 + \dfrac{R_1 + R_2}{A_{ol}(DC)R_2}(1 + j\omega\tau)} \right]$$

The term "1" in the round brackets in the equation above can be neglected. If ω is low "A" is high and kills the whole term. If ω is high the $j\omega\tau$ term dominates it. This approximation gives:-

$$\frac{V_{out}}{V_{in}} \approx \frac{R_1 + R_2}{R_2} \left[\frac{1}{1 + \dfrac{R_1 + R_2}{A_{ol}(DC) R_2} j\omega\tau} \right]$$

This is a first-order low-pass response so it can be compared with the standard low-pass response. This gives:-

$$\frac{V_{out}}{V_{in}} \approx K \frac{1}{1 + j\omega\tau'}$$

with $\quad K = \dfrac{R_1 + R_2}{R_2} \quad$ and $\quad \tau' = \dfrac{R_1 + R_2}{A_{ol}(DC) R_2} \tau$

The system is first-order low-pass with a DC gain of $(R_1 + R_2)/R_2$.

Consider the unity-gain bandwidth, i.e. the frequency at which the gain drops to one.

$$\left| \frac{V_{out}}{V_{in}} \right| = 1 = \frac{R_1 + R_2}{R_2} \left| \frac{1}{1 + \dfrac{R_1 + R_2}{A_{ol}(DC) R_2} j\omega\tau} \right|$$

$$\Rightarrow \left| 1 + \frac{R_1 + R_2}{A_{ol}(DC) R_2} j\omega\tau \right| = \frac{R_1 + R_2}{R_2}$$

$$\Rightarrow \text{(approximately)} \quad \frac{R_1 + R_2}{A_{ol}(DC) R_2} \omega\tau = \frac{R_1 + R_2}{R_2}$$

$$\Rightarrow \omega_{\text{unity gain}} = A_{ol}(DC)/\tau$$

This is exactly the same unity gain frequency as the op-amp itself. Therefore the overall frequency response is as shown by the solid line in Figure 18.7. The dotted line is the open-loop frequency response of the op-amp.

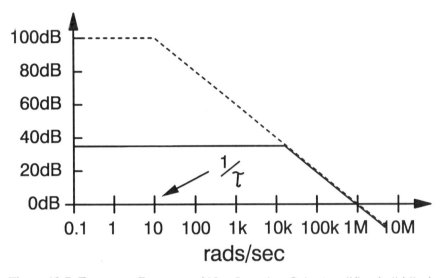

Figure 18.7: Frequency Response of Non-Inverting Gain Amplifier (solid line)

The response shown in Figure 18.7 is, in general, the sort of thing we expect to see in almost all op-amp circuits. The frequency response is determined by the external circuit but cannot escape the envelope of the open-loop response of the op-amp.

For example, suppose we make a simple differentiator using the circuit of Figure 18.8.

The usual analysis gives:−

$$\frac{v_{in}}{1/j\omega C} + \frac{v_{out}}{R} = 0$$

$$\Rightarrow v_{in}j\omega CR + v_{out} = 0$$

$$\Rightarrow \frac{v_{out}}{v_{in}} = -j\omega RC$$

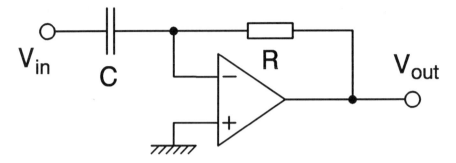

Figure 18.8: Simple Op-Amp Differentiator

The transfer function of a differentiator is:-

$$V_{out}/V_{in} = K j \omega$$

so its amplitude response is a straight line with a slope of $+20$dB/decade. The vertical position of the line is determined by the constant term, K. The graph of a perfect differentiator is shown as the solid line in Figure 18.9 while the dotted line is the response actually achieved. The chained line is the open loop gain of the op-amp.

You can see that the op-amp differentiator is a good approximation to "perfect" until it nears the open-loop gain of the op-amp. As the frequency increases above this intersection point the amplitude response is limited by the op-amp open-loop response.

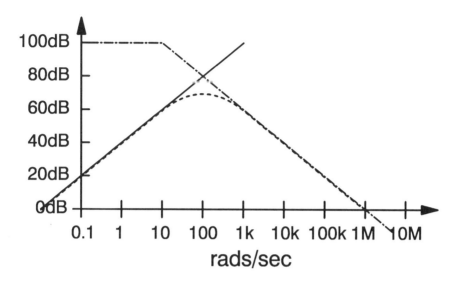

Figure 18.9: Differentiator Responses, perfect (solid), real-life(dotted)

QUESTIONS

18.1) A single pole amplifier is designed with negative feedback where 10% of the output voltage is fed back in series with the input voltage. If the amplifier open loop gain is 80dB and the cut off frequency is 10kHz, what is the closed loop gain and cut off frequency?

18.2) An operational amplifier has an open loop DC voltage gain of 60dB with three poles (in a way, similar to cutoff frequencies) at 1MHz, 100MHz and 200MHz. The final stage has an output impedance of 200Ω.

Draw the amplitude and phase Bode plots of the amplifier. What is its unity gain frequency? By finding the gain margin check whether it will be stable if configured as a unity-gain buffer.

If this op-amp was configured as an amplifier with overall gain, G, what would be the *minimum* value of G which would give a 10dB gain margin? What would be the bandwidth of the amplifier at this value of G?

It is now absolutely necessary to use this op-amp as a unity gain buffer. What additions would you make to the circuit to ensure a 60° phase margin when it is configured in this way? What would the unity gain frequency then be?

If the op-amp, compensated for unity-gain operation, was now used to make an amplifier with gain, G, as defined above, what would be the amplifier bandwidth?

18.3) A operational amplifier has an open loop DC voltage gain of 60dB with two poles at 100kHz and 100MHz. Draw the gain and phase Bode plots of the amplifier and hence estimate the frequency at which the open loop voltage gain is unity. What is the worst-case phase margin?

Using this operational amplifier design an inverting amplifier with a closed loop voltage gain of 26dB. You are told that a supply of 10kΩ and 1kΩ resistors are available. Use the Bode plots to estimate bandwidth of your amplifier.

Chapter 19

ACTIVE FILTERS

A filter is a frequency selective device which passes signals of certain frequencies and attenuates or blocks signals of other frequencies.

19.1 CLASSIFICATION

Low Pass	Passes low frequencies and blocks high frequencies.
High Pass	Passes high frequencies and blocks low frequencies.
Band Pass	Passes a band of frequencies and blocks those frequencies which are higher or lower than those in the band.
Band Reject	Blocks a band of frequencies and passes those frequencies which are higher or lower than those in the band.

19.2 PASSBAND

In the *passband* of a filter the voltage gain, V_{out}/V_{in}, is never more than 3dB below the maximum gain. Thus, at the edges of the passband, exactly *one half* of the maximum possible power is transmitted. The *bandwidth* of a filter is usually measured between the frequencies at which the gain is *exactly* 3dB less than the maximum. For a low-pass filter this is from DC to the passband edge. Bandwidth is not defined for a true high-pass filter.

The above is the only definition we shall use here but there exist other definitions of "passband" for other filters, such as band-stop filters or Chebyshev filters. These are beyond the scope of this book.

19.3 ACTIVE FILTER DESIGN USING OP-AMPS

The first consideration when designing an active filter using op-amps is to
check that we are not asking for more gain than the op-amp can supply. We
usually also ensure that there is a safety margin of at least 20dB. To make
this check we first draw out the bode plot of the op-amp open loop gain and
on the same graph draw our desired filter amplitude response. An example is
drawn in Figure 19.1.

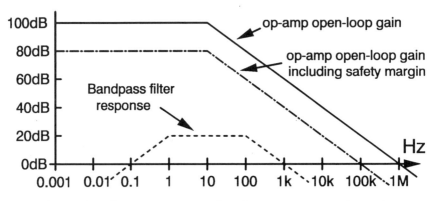

Figure 19.1: Op-Amp Response (solid), Filter Response (dotted),
Boundary (chained)

The example shows a bandpass filter with cutoff frequencies of 1Hz and
100Hz. The passband gain is 20dB so the gain at the edges of the passband is
17dB.

19.4 SINGLE OP-AMP ACTIVE FILTERS

Consider our old friend, the inverting amplifier, shown in Figure 19.2. The
difference is that now we will use *impedances* Z_1 and Z_2 instead of resistors.

Formally we would do a steady-state analysis with a complex phasor input.
Instead we will write down the usual result:-

$$\frac{v_{out}}{v_{in}} = \frac{-Z_2}{Z_1}$$

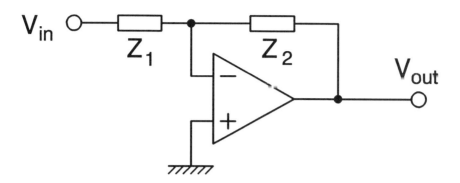

Figure 19.2: Circuit Diagram of Inverting Op-amp Amplifier

Assuming that Z_1 and Z_2 are not just resistors, this is a *complex transfer function*.

For example, suppose Z_1 is a capacitor, C, and Z_2 is a resistor, R. Then:-

$$\frac{v_{out}}{v_{in}} = \frac{-R}{1/j\omega C} = -j\omega RC$$

This is one of our standard responses (page 127) and has a $+20$dB/decade slope going through 0dB at $\omega = 1/RC$.

19.5 LAPLACE VARIABLE

It is likely that you have seen, in the Maths course associated with your Engineering, the *Laplace Transform*. These make much use of a variable "s". Everywhere in these notes $j\omega$ can be replaced by the Laplace variable "s". As well as "s" being equal to $j\omega$, "s" means "differentiate" and "1/s" means "integrate". The transfer function above is:-

$$\frac{v_{out}}{v_{in}} = -j\omega RC = -RCs \Rightarrow v_{out} = -RCs\,v_{in} = -RC\frac{dv_{in}}{dt}$$

Thus the circuit is a inverting differentiator with gain RC.

19.6 ANOTHER EXAMPLE

Suppose that, this time, Z_2 is a capacitor, C, and Z_1 is a resistor, R. Then:-

$$\frac{v_{out}}{v_{in}} = \frac{-1/j\omega C}{R} = \frac{-1}{j\omega\,RC} = \frac{-1}{RC}\frac{1}{s}$$

This is also a standard response, though not one we have seen before. It is a straight line with a -20dB/decade slope going through 0dB at $\omega = 1/RC$. Its phase response is $\tan^{-1}[\text{Im/Re}] = \tan^{-1}[-\infty] = -90°$

Looking at the form of the equation with "s" in it we find a term "1/s" so this is an inverting *integrator* with gain 1/RC.

19.7 ACTIVE BAND PASS FILTER

Suppose we let Z_1 be a capacitor, C_1, in *series* with a resistor of value R_1. Further, let Z_2 be a capacitor, C_2, in *parallel* with a resistor of value R_2. The resulting circuit is shown in Figure 19.3.

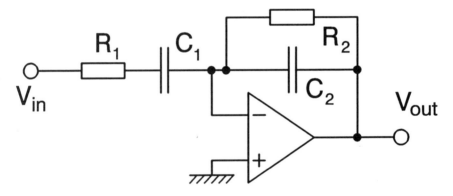

Figure 19.3: One type of Op-Amp Active Filter

The obvious equations give:-

$$Z_1 = R_1 + \frac{1}{j\omega C_1} = \frac{1 + j\omega\,R_1\,C_1}{j\omega\,C_1} \quad \text{and}$$

$$Z_2 = R_2 \parallel \frac{1}{j\omega C_2} = \frac{R_2/j\omega C_2}{R_2 + 1/j\omega C_2} = \frac{R_2}{1 + j\omega R_2 C_2}$$

As $v_{out}/v_{in} = -Z_2/Z_1$ we have:-

$$\frac{v_{out}}{v_{in}} = \left[\frac{-R_2}{R_1} \right] * \left[\frac{j\omega R_1 C_1}{1 + j\omega R_1 C_1} \right] * \left[\frac{1}{1 + j\omega R_2 C_2} \right]$$

The first of these three terms is a constant. The second is a *high-pass* function with cutoff $\omega_1 = 1/R_1 C_1$ while the third is a *low-pass* function with cutoff $\omega_2 = 1/R_2 C_2$.

Assuming $\omega_2 > \omega_1$, we get the Bode plots shown in Figure 19.4. (Note that the $180°$ phase shift due to the $-ve$ sign in the transfer function is not included in the phase graph in Figure 19.4).

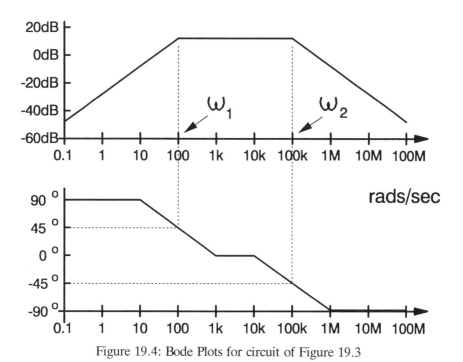

Figure 19.4: Bode Plots for circuit of Figure 19.3

19.8 NON-INVERTING OP-AMP BASED ACTIVE FILTER

The circuit of a non-inverting op-amp based active filter is shown in Figure 19.5. Here $Z_{1 \text{ to } 4}$ are *impedances*.

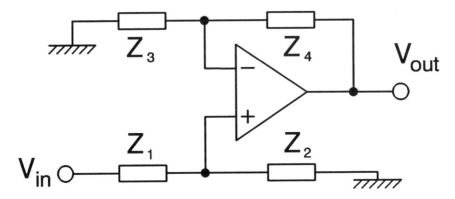

Figure 19.5: Circuit of Non-Inverting Op-Amp Active Filter

We apply the usual Ohm's Law type analysis to get:-

$$V_+ = \frac{Z_2}{Z_1 + Z_2} V_{in} \quad \text{and} \quad V_- = \frac{Z_3}{Z_3 + Z_4} V_{out}$$

Remembering that $V_+ = V_-$, these combine to give:-

$$\frac{V_{out}}{V_{in}} = \frac{Z_2 (Z_3 + Z_4)}{Z_3 (Z_1 + Z_2)}$$

Let Z_1 and Z_4 be resistors R_1 and R_4, respectively, and Z_2 and Z_3 be the impedances of capacitors C_2 and C_3, respectively. Then the circuit becomes that of Figure 19.6.

Substituting appropriately in the above equation gives:-

$$\frac{V_{out}}{V_{in}} = \frac{1 + R_4 C_3 j\omega}{1 + R_1 C_2 j\omega}$$

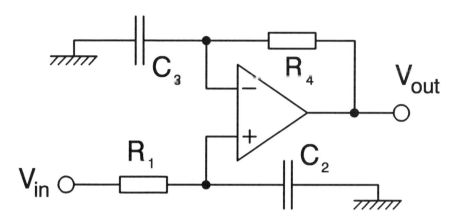

Figure 19.6: Op-Amp Active Filter

Letting $\tau_1 = R_4C_3$, $\tau_2 = R_1C_2$ and assuming that $1/\tau_1 < 1/\tau_2$, gives the slightly odd graph shown in Figure 19.7 when we plot the amplitude response.

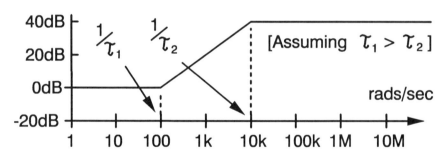

Figure 19.7: Op-Amp Active Filter Response

QUESTIONS

19.1)   For the circuit in Figure 19.8 show that the voltage gain is:-

$$A_v = \frac{Z_2(Z_3 + Z_4)}{Z_3(Z_1 + Z_2)}$$

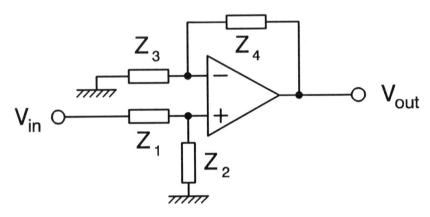

Figure 19.8: Op-amp Circuit using Impedances

Is this amplifier an inverting or non-inverting design?

Now if $Z_1 = 1\mu F$, $Z_2 = 1k\Omega$ and $Z_3 = Z_4 = 10k\Omega$, what type of filter results?

Give the full transfer function of the filter, v_{out}/v_{in}, and sketch its amplitude Bode Plot.

Calculate the passband gain in dB and the cutoff frequency in Hertz.

Find the gain in dB and the sign and magnitude in degrees of the phase shift relative to the input at a frequency of 20Hz.

19.2)   The circuit shown in Figure 19.9 is an active filter. How many poles has it? Calculate the passband gain in dB and the 3dB cut off frequency.

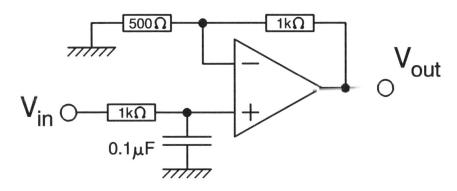

Figure 19.9: Op-Amp Active Filter Circuit

19.3)   Shown in Figure 19.10 is a simple op-amp circuit. Find its response. What does it do?

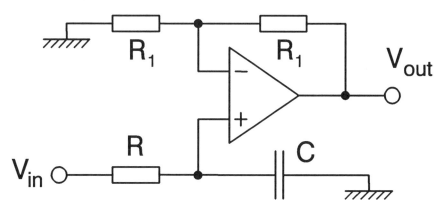

Figure 19.10: Op-amp Circuit.

19.4)   Design an op-amp circuit with the amplitude response shown in Figure 19.11.

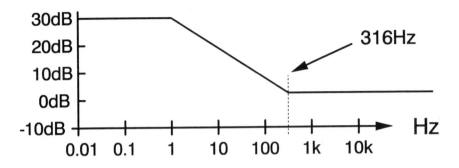

Figure 19.11: Required Response for Op-amp Circuit

19.5)   Suppose the circuit shown in Figure 19.12 was in a box and only the
        terminal marked "IN" and earth were available. If measurements
        were taken what would appear to be in the box?

        Hint:- Analyse the circuit in terms of current taken for a given AC
        voltage applied. Use phasors.

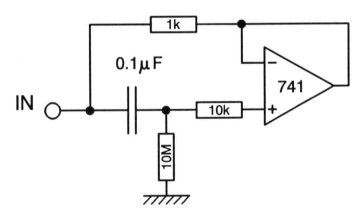

Figure 19.12: Op-amp Circuit.

Chapter 20

DC POWER SUPPLIES

The usual power supply available from the plug in the wall is 230-250V, 50Hz AC, but most electronic circuits need lower, DC, voltages, usually in the range 3V to about 15V. It is therefore not surprising that small DC power supplies are among the most ubiquitous of electronic circuits.

There are a number of methods that can be used to produce low voltage DC power from a mains input. The usual method which springs to mind involves a transformer, rectification and smoothing but other methods are also available.

In very old televisions the mains was often rectified with a single valve and a resistor potential divider gave the required low voltages. The resistors used were large (3 inch long cylinders of one inch diameter) and got *very* hot. Clearly the method was not at all efficient but, because there was no transformer, it was cheap. Also because there was no transformer the TV set innards were not isolated from the mains and so the chassis was often "live". Hence the use of bakelite knobs, etc.

Isolation transformers are still not always used in televisions so you should note that the chassis of TV sets can still be live. There was recently a case of a student modifying a TV set to use headphones. The outer shield of the jackplug was connected to the chassis ...

DC voltages are often obtained today from "switched-mode power supplies". These operate at high efficiencies (over 85%) and are light and cheap.

The DC power supplies we will consider as part of this course are the normal type found in almost all consumer electronic equipment. A block diagram of such a power supply is shown in Figure 20.1.

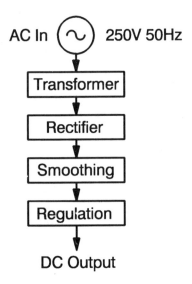

Figure 20.1: Block Diagram of Simple DC Power Supply

The transformer is just the usual thing. It is rather expensive, very heavy by comparison with other components, gets hot and is altogether rather undesirable. However, it is the usual "voltage changer".

20.1 RECTIFICATION

20.1.1 Half-Wave Rectifier

The most simple form of rectification is the half-wave rectifier. We will represent the output of the transformer by V_s and we will have a purely resistive load, R_L. Then the circuit and the resulting waveforms are as shown in Figures 20.2 and 20.3.

This is not a very good output waveform; we get nothing at all for half the time. However it is about as cheap as you'll get.

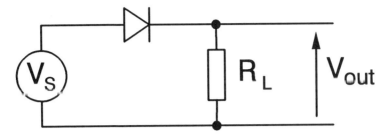

Figure 20.2: Circuit Diagram of Half Wave Rectifier

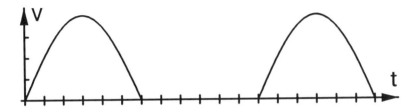

Figure 20.3: Output Waveform of Half Wave Rectifier

20.1.2 Full-Wave Rectifier

There are two main types of full-wave rectifiers. The first, shown in Figure 20.4, requires a centre-tapped transformer. Note that the secondary winding can be viewed as two secondaries in series, *only one of which conducts current at any one time*. The output waveform is shown in Figure 20.5.

If, for example, we wanted the magnitude of the output waveform (zero to peak) to be *equal* to the magnitude of the waveform input to the transformer, *each* of the two series secondary windings would to have the same number of turns as the primary winding.

Each of the two series secondary windings conducts current in only one direction. Therefore there is a DC component to the current through the windings. This can make the transformer a bit unhappy.

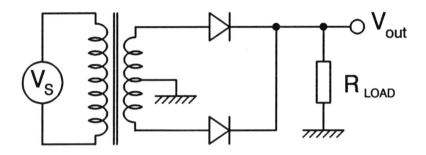

Figure 20.4: Full-Wave Rectifier using Centre Tapped Transformer

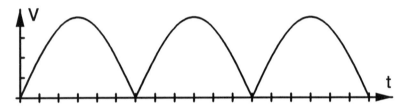

Figure 20.5: Output Signal of a Full-Wave Rectifier

A far better full-wave rectifier is the *bridge rectifier* shown in Figure 20.6.

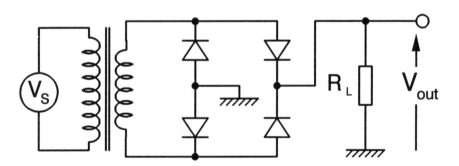

Figure 20.6: Full-Wave Bridge Rectifier

The output waveform is exactly that shown in Figure 20.5. Clearly four diodes are required instead of two but only one secondary winding is used and it is used all the time. At any one time the current in the load resistor is also flowing through *two* diodes so there is a 1.4V voltage drop across the bridge.

DO NOT TRY TO BRIDGE RECTIFY THE MAINS DIRECTLY!!. Apart from being dangerous it will work only if we do not earth one of the DC outputs. If you do earth one DC output the diodes will blow. If you try it without earthing one of the DC outputs, both DC outputs will be at mains potentials.

20.2 ROOT MEAN SQUARE

The output of a typical power supply is not an absolutely constant DC voltage. It will very slightly, usually at a frequency equal to, or twice, the frequency of the mains, i.e. at 50Hz or 100Hz. We will be interested in the RMS output voltage so a definition plus a couple of useful special cases would be in order.

For a periodic waveform, $V(t)$, with period T we have:-

$$V_{rms} = \left[\frac{\int_0^T v^2(t)\,dt}{T} \right]^{\frac{1}{2}}$$

For a sine wave, $V(t) = A\sin(t)$ which gives:-

$$V_{rms} = \left[\int_0^{2\pi} \frac{A^2 \sin^2(t)\,dt}{2\pi} \right]^{\frac{1}{2}}$$

Now $\displaystyle \int_0^{2\pi} A^2 \sin^2(t)\,dt = A^2 \int_0^{2\pi} \frac{1 - \cos(2t)}{2}\,dt$

$$= A^2 \int_0^{2\pi} \frac{1}{2}\,dt - \frac{A^2}{2} \int_0^{2\pi} \cos(2t)\,dt$$

$$= A^2 * \frac{2\pi}{2} - 0 = \pi A^2$$

Thus:— $$V_{rms} = \left[\int_0^{2\pi} \frac{A^2 \sin^2(t)\, dt}{2\pi} \right]^{\frac{1}{2}} = \sqrt{\pi A^2 / 2\pi} = \frac{A}{\sqrt{2}}$$

Now let's do the rms calculations on a sawtooth waveform like that shown in Figure 20.7.

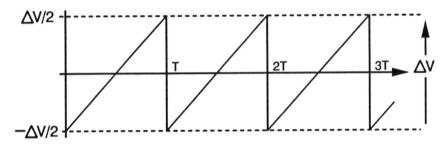

Figure 20.7: Sawtooth Waveform

Note that this waveform is balanced about zero, i.e. it has the same amount above the x-axis as below. Mathematically, over the region $0 < t < T$, this graph is described by:—

$$V(t) = \Delta V \left[\frac{t}{T} - \frac{1}{2} \right]$$

We calculate its rms value as:—

$$V_{rms} = \left[\frac{\int_0^T \Delta V^2 \left(\frac{t}{T} - \frac{1}{2} \right)^2 dt}{T} \right]^{\frac{1}{2}}$$

$$\text{Now:} - \int_0^T \left[\frac{t}{T} - \frac{1}{2} \right]^2 dt = \int_0^T \frac{t^2}{T^2} dt - \int_0^T \frac{t}{T} dt + \int_0^T \frac{1}{4} dt$$

$$= \frac{T}{3} - \frac{T}{2} + \frac{T}{4} = \frac{T}{12}$$

$$\text{This gives:} - \quad V_{rms} = \left[\frac{\int_0^T \Delta V^2 \left(\frac{t}{T} - \frac{1}{2} \right)^2 dt}{T} \right]^{\frac{1}{2}}$$

$$= \left[\Delta V^2 * \frac{T}{12\,T} \right]^{\frac{1}{2}} = \frac{\Delta V}{2\sqrt{3}}$$

These equations will be useful later for calculating power.

The *average output voltage* is defined as:$- \quad V_{av} = (V_{max} - V_{min})/2$

The *ripple factor* is defined as:$- \quad$ Ripple Factor $= (V_{rms}/V_{av}) = \dfrac{\Delta V}{2\sqrt{3}V_{av}}$

20.3 FILTERING OR SMOOTHING

After the AC transformer output has been rectified we either have a half-wave rectified waveform or a full-wave rectified waveform. Neither can be said to be DC. We now need to *smooth* the waveform; to smooth the peaks into the troughs so that we get a nearer constant output voltage.

The simplest form of smoothing is a capacitor set up as shown in Figure 20.8.

Note that although this type of smoothing used to be very common, the *pulses* of current which it draws from the transformer secondary result in *pulses* of current being drawn by the primary from the mains supply. These pulses cause harmonics in the mains and upset the electricity supply authorities. For this reason, under new EEC directives this form of smoothing will not be permitted in commercially designed equipment. The widespread introduction of switched-mode power supplies has also caused a reduction in the use of this kind of filter but, all that aside, this type of smoothing is the simplest possible and the only one that will be examined here. The principles behind its analysis apply equally to any other smotthing technique.

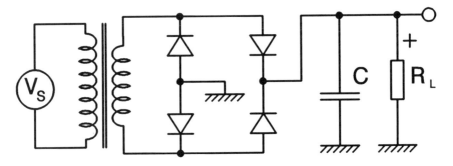

Figure 20.8: Capacitor Smoothing.

There is at least one little problem with this circuit which occurs at switch-on. If the switch-on time is unfortunately chosen the transformer will try to give a maximum output voltage at the very time the capacitor is totally discharged. The result will be a huge current surge through the diodes which tend to vapourise. The cure is a small resistor is series with each diode or in series with the rectifier output. Sometimes the resistance of the transformer secondary winding will do. That problem aside, the output waveform should look like that shown in Figure 20.9.

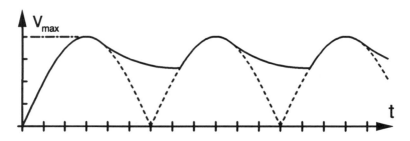

Figure 20.9: Output Waveform using Simple Capacitor Smoothing

The capacitor charges to V_{max}, the transformer output voltage peak (assuming no voltage drop across the diodes). The diodes then stop the capacitor voltage following the transformer output voltage on the way down and the capacitor discharges through the load resistor, R_L. Clearly the discharge curve will be exponential and will, in fact, be:-

$$V_{out} = V_{max} e^{-t/R_L C}$$

It is far too complicated to work out the variation in output voltage from this graph. Instead we will start making the usual gross approximations.

Let us consider the discharge slope. The slope is given by the *differential* of V_{out}:-

$$\frac{dV_{out}}{dt} = \frac{-V_{max}}{R_L C} e^{-t/R_L C}$$

The maximum slope occurs at t=0 and is $-V_{max}/(R_L C)$.

We will take the approximation shown in Figure 20.10. Here we have taken the gradient of the discharge curve to be the maximum value of the true gradient. We start this linear approximation to the discharge curve at V_{max} and continue it for time T, the period. The result is therefore a *saw-tooth* waveform.

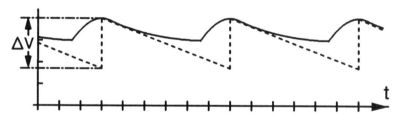

Figure 20.10: Approximation to Output Waveform

Using this approximation the maximum output is V_{max}. The minimum is:-

$$V_{min} = V_{max} - [V_{max}/(R_L C)] * T$$

The variable, ΔV, is defined as:-

$$\Delta V = V_{max} - V_{min} = V_{max} T/(R_L C)$$

The section on root mean squares (p142) tells us that the rms output ripple in rms terms is $\Delta V/2\sqrt{3}$.

Under this approximation

$$V_{av} = \frac{V_{max} - V_{min}}{2} = V_{max} - \frac{V_{max} T}{2 R_L C}$$

We now have $V_{out} = V_{av} + \Delta V$ so

$$V_{out(rms)}^2 = V_{av}^2 + [\Delta V/2\sqrt{3}]^2 = V_{max}^2 \left[1 - \frac{T}{R_L C} + \frac{T^2}{3 R_L^2 C^2} \right]$$

If we pretend the "3" in the right-most part of the above equation is actually a "4" (not too dreadful an approximation compared to some of the others!) we get:-

$$V_{out(rms)}^2 \approx V_{max}^2 \left[1 - \frac{T}{2 R_L C} \right]^2 \Rightarrow V_{out(rms)} = V_{max} \left[1 - \frac{T}{2 R_L C} \right]$$

The above is a fair approximation if $R_L C \gg T$. More importantly, it *over* estimates the output voltage variation. Therefore we can be sure that the real variation will be *less* than this approximate value.

The so-called DC output from this smoothing stage is not very good. We can get real DC if either T is zero (so we are working with mains at infinite frequency), R_L is infinite (no load) or C is infinite (and infinite capacitors are hard to find).

The first option, decreasing T, is actually quite good and is extensively used (along with other techniques) in high performance power supplies. Since the transformer would also have to work at higher frequency, advantage could also be taken of the fact that, for a given power level, transformers decrease in size as the frequency increases. This decreases weight, cost, etc.

20.4 REGULATION WITH ZENERS

If we are looking for a low ripple voltage, then after the smoothing stage must come a *regulator*. Probably the simplest regulator is a *Zener Diode*.

A Zener Diode is a special kind of diode which we normally drive *backwards*. That is, we increase the *reverse* bias voltage across it until it is forced to carry current the wrong way. Zener diodes are also known as *avalanche diodes*. They have the voltage/current characteristic shown in Figure 20.11.

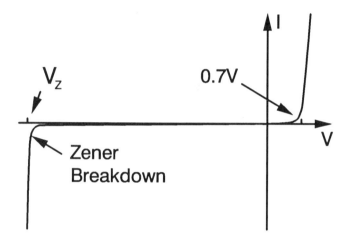

Figure 20.11: Voltage/Current Relationship for Zener Diode

This is, in fact, the normal diode characteristic but here the diode has been heavily doped so that its reverse breakdown voltage occurs at a lower voltage. The interesting part of the characteristic is on the left side. The voltage V_Z is the *Zener Voltage*.

After the zener voltage has been reached the diode starts to conduct large amounts of current. If the current through the zener is not limited by the external circuit the result is a dead zener.

Note that the graph of voltage against current in Figure 20.11 is not vertical above the zener voltage though it is steep. The *inverse* of the gradient of that part of the characteristic is the zener *resistance*, R_Z. A steep slope has a large gradient and so represents a low resistance. We can model a zener as a "perfect zener" which conducts infinite current above its zener voltage in series with a resistor of value R_Z.

A zener diode can be used in circuits like that shown in Figure 20.12.

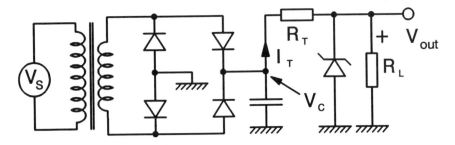

Figure 20.12: Power Supply using Zener Regulator

In this scheme the average current drawn from the transformer is *constant*, irrespective of the load resistance, R_L. Depending on the value of R_L, the current *either* goes through the load *or* through the zener.

The current from the transformer is given by $I_T = (V_C - V_{out})/R_i$. This current is shared by the load and the zener.

If the load resistance is low then nearly all the current will go through the load. If the load resistance becomes *too* low then no current will go through the zener and excess voltage will be dropped across R_i. Thus the output voltage will fall.

If the load resistance rises then more and more current will flow through the zener until, when the load is an open circuit, *all* the current goes through the zener. The power dissipated in the zener will then be at its maximum of $I_T * V_Z$. The designer must ensure that the zener is capable of dissipating this power.

As the load current varies the zener current varies (more load current implies less zener current). As the zener current rises/falls the voltage across it rises/falls (because of the zener resistance). Thus the output voltage varies with current; the more output current the lower the output voltage.

We define the concept of *percentage regulation* as:-

$$\text{Percentage regulation} = \frac{V_{out(max)} - V_{out(min)}}{V_Z} * 100 \text{ %}$$

In other circuits we replace V_Z by the nominal output voltage.

Straightforward zener diode regulation is not very great, though it is a whole lot better than none at all. It has the following disadvantages:-

1) Low efficiency. Constant power is drawn from the transformer even if there is no real output current.

2) Variable Output Voltage. Because of R_Z the output voltage varies with output current

3) Temperature Variation. The value of V_Z varies with temperature. For low zener voltages (less than about 6V) temperature coefficients are negative (increasing temperature implies decreasing zener voltage). For zener voltages above about 6V the temperature coefficients are positive. Because the crossover occurs at about 6V temperature compensated zeners tend to be about this value.

4) Zeners are *very* noisy. They are so good at producing electrical noise that they are used as noise sources.

To improve on zeners as regulators we must turn to transistors. The simplest transistor/zener based regulators involve a *pass transistor*.

20.5 REGULATION USING PASS TRANSISTORS

The circuit diagram of a voltage regulator designed using a pass transistor is given in Figure 20.13.

Here we have a standard transformer/rectifier/smoothing power supply which will provide a very crude DC voltage with high ripple.

The idea of this circuit is that resistor R_i and the zener diode provide a fairly constant voltage of V_Z on the base of the transistor. The transistor is set up as an emitter follower so $V_{out} = V_Z - 0.7$. In general, this works fine and the results are much better than for the simple zener-only circuit.

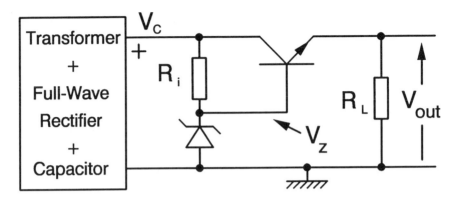

Figure 20.13: Circuit Diagram of Voltage Regulator Using a Pass Transistor

Note that when designing the supply we must ensure that *at all times* V_C is greater than the rated output voltage plus 0.7V. At maximum output current V_C will tend to fall and *still* V_C must be greater than $V_{out(rated)}$ + 0.7. For this reason we usually design the transformer and smoothing such that V_C is at least two or three volts greater than $V_{out(rated)}$. The side effect when we do this is, of course, that the voltage across the pass transistor increases and so its power dissipation increases.

Advantages

1) Efficiency. If no output current is required the pass transistor tends to turn OFF and so it dissipates very little power. The zener takes an almost constant, but relatively small, current irrespective of output current so this complete circuit dissipates very little power if there is no output current.

2) Low output impedance. The transistor will attempt to ensure that the output voltage is constant irrespective of output current. This can be a disadvantage because the transistor can be a little over-enthusiastic and burn out. Over-current protection is usually required.

Disadvantages/Problems

1) The resistor/zener combination supplies an output current, I_B, which is the base current of the transistor and should therefore be fairly small. However, power transistors tend to have low β values (10?) so if the output current is to be significant the base current may be fairly large.

For example, if the supply is to be capable of delivering 10A and $\beta=10$, the base current will be 1A. Perhaps more importantly, the variation of the base current as the output current varies from 0 to 10A will be 0 to 1A. This will cause fairly large variations in V_Z. It's still much better than just using an enormous zener by itself (the ripple is divided approximately by transistor β).

2) The zener current is greatly set by I_B *and* $(V_C - V_Z)/R_i$. As the value of V_C may vary quite significantly there is an undesirable effect on V_Z. This effect can be minimised by using two zener regulated supplies. The first supply is set to produce, say, $V_{out(rated)} + 4V$ and this becomes the supply voltage for the second zener which is set to produce $V_{out(rated)} + 0.7V$. This trick is shown in Figure 20.14.

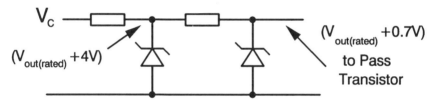

Figure 20.14: Double Zener Regulation

3) The pass transistor gets very hot for maximum output current and will almost certainly require a heat sink.

4) If there is *no* output current, i.e. $R_L = \infty$, the leakage through the pass transistor can cause V_{out} to float up to V_C. For this reason it is conventional to place a "bleeder" resistor across the supply output so that some output current is always drawn.

5) Temperature variation. The zener diode voltage, V_Z, has a temperature coefficient. As the ambient temperature varies the output voltage will vary.

Some of these problems can be reduced if an op-amp based supply is used.

20.6 POWER SUPPLY REGULATION USING AN OP-AMP

Consider the circuit shown in Figure 20.15.

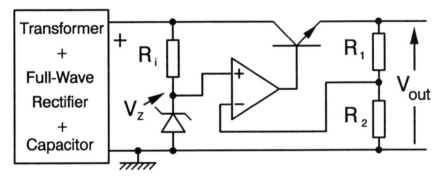

Figure 20.15: Voltage Regulator Using a Pass Transistor and Op-Amp

In this circuit a conventional zener diode provides a reference voltage, usually around 6V because 6V zeners have a near zero temperature coefficient. If required, a double zener supply such as shown in Figure 140 may be used to improve the regulation of this reference voltage.

The op-amp compares the reference voltage with that on the potential divider.

If $V_{out} R_2/(R_1 + R_2) < V_Z$ the op-amp output goes higher so driving the pass transistor harder ON and increasing the output voltage.

If $V_{out} R_2/(R_1 + R_2) > V_Z$ the op-amp output goes lower so turning the pass transistor more OFF and decreasing the output voltage.

This form of regulation is probably the most frequently used, particularly since most of the components can be, and have been, fabricated together on a single integrated circuit.

Chips such as the 78 and 79 series have the op-amp, zener, resistors and power transistor in a single three-legged package. The "78" series give positive output voltages and the "79" series give negative voltages. A "7805", for example gives 15V while a "7924" gives −24V. These devices can cope with a maximum current of 1A and also include short circuit protection. How do you think they do that?

Note that regulator chips are often specified as, for example, $V_{in(max)} = V_{out} + 8V$ and Iout(max) = 1A. However, you *can't* have both at once because there is also a power dissipation specification which might be $P_{max} = 2.5W$. If the voltage across the device is maximum (8V) *and* the current is maximum (1A) then the dissipation will be 8W. This point has been the death of many student power supplies!

20.7 EXAMPLE

The basic circuit for a regulated power supply is given in Figure 20.16.

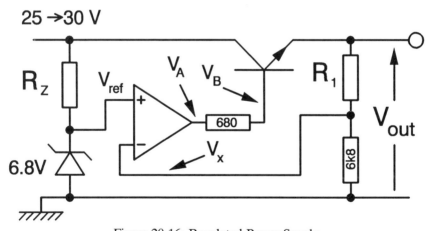

Figure 20.16: Regulated Power Supply

It is to be capable of supplying a (relatively) constant fifteen volts at a maximum output current of one amp. The zener diode shown is rated 6.8V and, to minimise self-heating, should dissipate between 20mW and 30mW. The incoming voltage will be between 25 and 30 volts, depending on loading and other factors.

Take all diode drops to be exactly 0.7V and $\beta = 100$ for all transistors. Initially assume the op-amp to be ideal.

Find appropriate values for R_1 and R_Z.

We need R_1 to be such a value that, when $V_{out} = 15$, $V_x = 6.8V$. This gives $R_1 = 8.2k\Omega$.

R_z must limit the power dissipation in the zener to between 20 and 30mW. Thus it must limit the zener *current* to between 2.94mA and 4.41mA. The voltage across R_z varies between $(30 - 6.8) = 23.2$ and $(25 - 6.8) = 18.2$. Taking the average current and average voltage gives $R_z = 5.63k\Omega$. Using the nearest standard value, $R_z = 5.6k\Omega$, and checking the zener power dissipation, we get $P_{max} = 28.17mW$ and $P_{min} = 22.1mW$, both in range.

Find V_a (the op-amp output voltage) and V_b (the voltage on the base of T1) when the output current is zero.

First consider zero output current (neglect the 1mA current through R_1). $V_{out} = 15V$ and V_b must be 0.7V greater than this. Thus $V_b = 15.7V$. There will be almost no base current in T1 so there will be no voltage drop across the 680Ω resistor and hence $V_a = 15.7V$ also.

Find V_a and V_b when the output current is one amp.

Now consider full load conditions, one amp output current. Because we are assuming a constant diode drop of 0.7V, we still have $V_b = 15.7V$. However, the base current of T1 will now be $I_E/(\beta + 1) = 1/101$ amps and this must flow through the 680Ω resistor. Thus $V_a = 15.7 + 680/101 = 22.43V$.

Find the maximum power dissipated in T1 under full specified load conditions.

The maximum possible power dissipated in T1 would occur when the input voltage was highest (30V) and the output current was maximum (1A). Under these conditions the voltage *across* T1 will be $30 - 15 = 15V$ and the

current through it will be 1A. Thus the maximum power dissipation will be 15W.

Now include the following additional factors:-

1) The zener diode is rated at 6.8V, $\pm 5\%$ at 20°C. It has a temperature coefficient of $+3mV/°C$. We will make the (rash) assumption that the power dissipated in the zener does not change its temperature.

2) The op-amp remains ideal with the exception that it has a DC gain of 5000.

3) The resistors employed have a 2% tolerance, i.e. their actual values may be up to 2% greater or 2% less than stated. They are temperature independent.

The whole circuit must operate over the temperature range 0°C to 70°C with an output load current of anywhere between zero and one amp.

Calculate the maximum and minimum values of V_{ref}, the voltage on the op-amp non-inverting input terminal.

V_{ref} will be highest when the zener starts highest and is hottest. The highest zener value will be $6.8 + 5\% = 7.14V$. The maximum temperature is 70°, 50° above the reference temperature of 20°. Thus the zener voltage will be raised by a further $50 * 3mV = 150mV$. The final, maximum, zener value will be $V_{ref(max)} = 7.14 + 0.15 = 7.29V$.

By a similar argument, the minimum value will be $V_{ref(min)} = (6.8 * 0.95) + (-20 * 3mV) = 6.4V$

V_x, the voltage on the op-amp inverting input terminal, can be calculated as $K V_{out}$ but K varies due to resistor inaccuracies. Find the minimum and maximum value of K.

We have that $V_x = V_{out} * R_2/(R_1 + R_2)$. Hence $K = R_2/(R_1 + R_2)$. Resistors can vary by $\pm 2\%$ so we maximise K by maximising R_2 and minimising R_1.

This gives:— $$K_{max} = \frac{6.8 * 1.02}{(6.8 * 1.02) + (8.2 * 0.98)} = 0.463265$$

Similarly $$K_{min} = \frac{6.8 * 0.98}{(6.8 * 0.98) + (8.2 * 1.02)} = 0.443439$$

Give an expression for V_a in terms of V_{ref} and V_x.

$$V_a = A(V_+ - V_-) = A(V_{ref} - V_x) = 5000(V_{ref} - K V_{out})$$

Derive an expression relating $(V_a - V_{out})$ to diode forward voltage drop and the power supply output current, I_{out}.

The voltage $V_a - V_{out}$ varies with output current according to:-

$$V_a - V_{out} = 0.7 + 680\,I_B = 0.7 + 680 * I_{out}/(\beta + 1) = 0.7 + 6.73267 * I_{out}$$

Thus $\quad V_{out} = V_a - 0.7 - 6.73267 * I_{out}$

$\Rightarrow V_{out} = 5000(V_{ref} - K V_{out}) - 0.7 - 6.73267 * I_{out}$

This gives:— $$V_{out} = \frac{5000\,V_{ref} - 0.7 - 6.73267 * I_{out}}{1 + 5000\,K}$$

Hence, or otherwise, calculate the minimum and maximum values of V_{out} as component values alter, temperature varies and output current changes.

To get the *maximum* V_{out} we should *maximise* V_{ref}, *minimise* I_{out} and *minimise* K. If we do this we obtain:-

$$V_{out(max)} = \frac{5000 * 7.29 - 0.7 - 6.73267 * 0}{1 + 5000 * 0.443439} = 16.432 \text{ volts}$$

To get the *minimum* V_{out} we should *minimise* V_{ref}, *maximise* I_{out} and *maximise* K. If we do this we obtain:-

$$V_{out(min)} = \frac{5000 * 6.4 - 0.7 - 6.73267 * 1}{1 + 5000 * 0.463265} = 13.806 \text{ volts}$$

NOTES

1) Note the large possible range in output voltage. To improve this we could add a potentiometer to remove the inaccuracies due to manufacturing imperfections in the zener diode and the resistors. However, we will have to be a bit more cunning than that to sort out the problems due to temperature.

2) The 680Ω resistor is only there to make the question a bit harder! We would not normally have this resistor present.

QUESTIONS

20.1) For the DC power supply illustrated in Figure 20.17, calculate the percentage ripple on the voltage across the capacitor and the percentage regulation of the voltage across the load. A 12V zener diode with $R_Z = 2\Omega$ is used. The pass transistor has $\beta = 100$. $I_{load(min)} = 400$mA, $I_{load(max)} = 500$mA

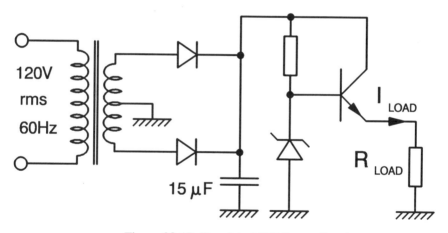

Figure 20.17: Regulated DC Power Supply

20.2) A well regulated 15V power supply is to be designed. The problem is given to an engineer and he decides to use the normal circuit he once heard about in lectures. This circuit uses a pass transistor, a big fellow like a 2N3055, controlled by an op-amp. The op-amp compares the output voltage (or a fraction of it) with a reference and controls the pass transistor so the difference is minimised. Reasoning that amplifying the difference further would improve the output voltage accuracy, the engineer modifies the standard circuit to become that shown in Figure 20.18.

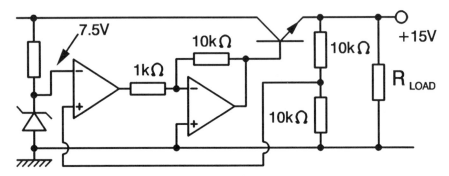

Figure 20.18: Regulated Power Supply Circuit(?)

Assuming that the zener reference voltage is correct and stable pass comment on his reasoning. 741 op-amps are used (100dB DC gain, Gain-Bandwidth of 1MHz) and the big pass-transistor used as an emitter follower has a gain-bandwidth of 100kHz. Both the op-amps and the transistor have first order low pass responses.

Hint:- Check for stability.

20.3) We need a voltage source (or something which is a fairly close
approximation) which will supply 5V at 1A. We have available some
not-specially-accurate but stable zener diodes rated 7.5V, some 741
op-amps and a packet of ZTX651 transistors (moderately hefty NPN
devices that will be OK for at least a couple of amps current).
Unfortunately, high current transistors have a poor β (the best we can
assume is $\beta = 15$) and a high leakage current (but no greater than
$100\mu A$). We have a good selection of resistors and potentiometers
(pre-sets) available too. The power supply we have available gives
11V DC off-load but has an internal resistance of 2Ω. Come up with a
circuit which will produce our 5V supply and find the variation of the
supply voltage with changing load.

What is the maximum power dissipated in the transistor(s)? Given
that ZTX651 transistors have a maximum power dissipation of 1.5W
and that this is a "homer" so we are not going to buy any more
transistors, how can we modify the circuit so it will not burn out the
output transistor(s).

Note that there is a phenomenon known as "current hogging". This
happens when a number of transistors are connected in parallel and
are supposed to share a load current. Usually one device takes a little
more than its mates (mismatch), gets a little hotter so takes more
current, gets even hotter, ... , burns out. This leaves more current for
the others which get a little hotter ....

It would be nice if your circuit didn't do this.

Chapter 21

PROBLEMS

In this Chapter are a number of "problems". These are seen as distinct from the "questions" given at the end of many of the previous chapters because they are often not related only to the material given in this book. Quite a number of them are "design" questions and some require common sense and an awareness of what goes on in the everyday world.

Best of luck!

Problem 1

How does one turn on and off the hall light with two switches? And with *three* switches?

Problem 2

Design a fuel gauge for a car. Remember that the battery voltage varies from about 11V to 16V. Also, we don't want the needle swinging about all over the place as we drive over bumps.

Problem 3

Using a single transistor and some diodes and resistors, design a three input NOR gate. Comment on its logic thresholds (the maximum recognisable logic 0 and the minimum recognisable logic 1).

Problem 4

A cheap hairdryer has two heat settings (three if you count "OFF"). How does it work?

Problem 5

Design a circuit which causes a light to go off 10 seconds *after* the switch is opened. (Like a courtesy light in a car). No 555 timers!

Problem 6

When a trailer lighting board is connected to a car its lights are normally connected in parallel with the car lights. The exceptions are the indicators which are driven in such a manner that the increase in load caused by the extra bulb drastically alters the flash rate. Design a system to drive indicators on a trailer without loading down the normal car indicators.

Problem 7

Design a circuit which will set off an alarm (or light an indicator) if a bulb dies on a car.

Problem 8

Light bulbs have a low resistance when cold and a high resistance when hot. Therefore, when the thing is switched on there is a big current surge before the current settles to its usual value. That's why bulbs always blow just as you switch them on. Design a circuit to reduce the current surge on switch-on.

Problem 9

In the normal car the high voltage required by the spark plugs is produced by the coil, which is just a step up transformer (many more turns on its secondary than its primary). Using the "points" (or "contact breaker") in the distributor, the battery is first connected to the primary and then disconnected. The principle is the same in most electronic systems; in those the contact breaker is just replaced by a semiconductor switch "fired" by some other sensor. The old-fashioned, simple, circuit is shown in Figure 21.1

When the contact breaker is closed the capacitor (still called a "condenser" in cars) is discharged and the current in the primary rises slowly, with its rate of increase limited by the primary inductance. This slow change in primary current causes a relatively low output voltage in the secondary, not enough to cause a spark. However, when the contact breakers are *opened* the circuit becomes an underdamped oscillating RLC circuit (see the example in section

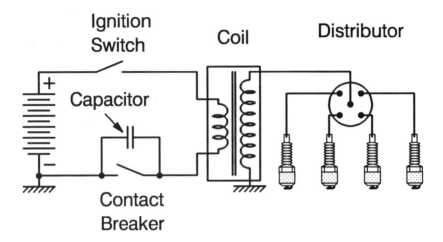

Figure 21.1: Car ignition wiring circuit

11.8 on page 107). The coil current rapidly falls to zero, goes negative, returns to zero and then becomes positive and so on. This causes a great big spark in the secondary which is fed to the appropriate spark plug by the rotor arm inside the distributor.

There is a potential problem with this system. If the ignition is turned on but the engine is not started, and the points happen to be closed, a DC current flows in the coil primary. To work well as an ignition system the primary resistance should be low so this current will be high. After some time the coil will overheat and burn out. Design a circuit which will turn off the ignition coil primary if the ignition is left on but the engine is not running.

By swapping the primary connections the spark voltage pulse can be made either positive-going or negative going. Which polarity would be better on the spark plug centre pin?

Often the ignition spark causes interference in the car radio. This can be reduced by the addition of a capacitor between one of the coil primary terminals and ground. To which terminal should the capacitor be connected? Should a big or small capacitor be used?

Problem 10

All the circuits given below are wrong. Why?

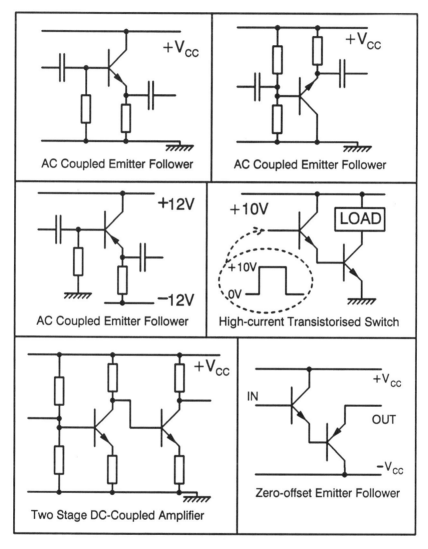

Figure 21.2: **BAD CIRCUITS!!**

Problem 11

In the circuit shown in Figure 21.3 the transformer turns ratio is 5:1, the transistor β is 25 and the transformer *secondary* DC resistance is 1Ω. Calculate the quiescent voltages on the three transistor terminals and comment on the circuit.

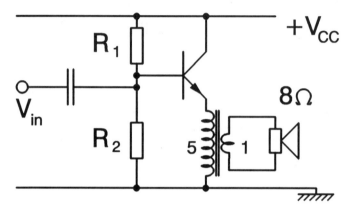

Figure 21.3: CC Amplifier using transformer

Problem 12

We have a bridge which bends a bit when loaded and we would like to measure the degree of deflection. We firstly want to set off an alarm if the deflection exceeds a set amount and secondly measure the degree of deflection. How?

Problem 13

Design an instrument that will determine whether the fridge light does, in fact, go out when the door is shut.

Problem 14

We want a transistor amplifier with the amplitude bode plot shown in Figure 21.4. The available transistor has $\beta = 100$ and $h_{ie} = 800\Omega$. The load capacitance is 100pF. What is a sensible value for C_{in}?

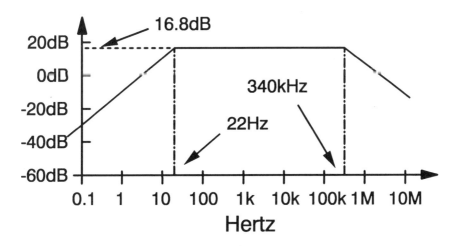

Figure 21.4: Required Amplifier Bode Plot

Problem 15

A **solenoid** is very like a relay but the required output "action" is a movement, rather than the change of position of an electrical switch. It is a multi-turn coil wound round a non-ferrous tube. Inside the tube is a movable iron (often ferrite) core. When current flows in the coil a magnetic field is set up which pulls the iron core into the centre of the coil. Thus the incoming current produces a small, linear, movement which is used to perform some other function such as turning on a valve. When the current is removed a spring returns the core to its at-rest position. Solenoids are normally voltage driven with the steady-state current being limited by the coil resistance.

We have a solenoid which is rated at 12V but will actually pull-in at 10V and hold in at 5V. We wish to operate it at 0.5Hz. We have a high-impedance 0.5Hz, 0→5V waveform but only a single 6V battery for a power source. Design a circuit which will operate the solenoid as specified.

Problem 16

Shown in Figure 21.5 are four circuits, each of which is intended to work as a amplifier for a 100kHz signal. Assume that the transistor is easily capable of working at that frequency and that its β is very high. Assume also that the DC bias has been correctly set. Arrange these circuits in order of merit and explain your reasoning.

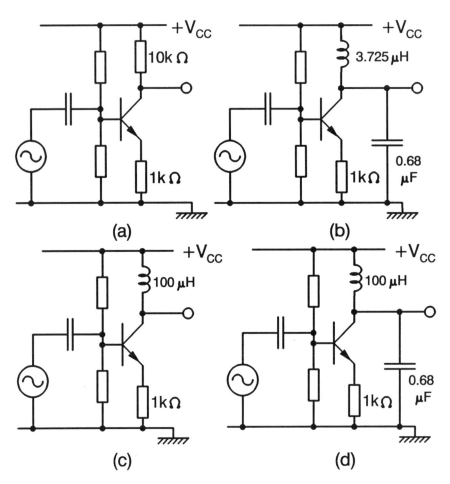

Figure 21.5: Four 100kHz Amplifiers.

Problem 17

In some electrical equipment available these days one finds touch switches. These do not move when pressed and contain no moving parts. There are two main types. One operates when it detects the resistance of a human body to ground and the other operates when it detects the capacitance of the human body to ground. Design (conceptually) two touch switches, one resistive and one capacitive.

Problem 18

A *tachometer* in a vehicle measures the number of revolutions completed by the vehicles engine in a minute. In other words, it measures r.p.m. Design a tachometer for a conventional petrol engined car. Does the number of engine cylinders affect your circuit? How would you tackle the problem for a diesel engined car?

Problem 19

Shown in Figure 21.6 are two radio frequency amplifiers. They are, basically, identical but their bias circuits are different. Comment on the merits of each.

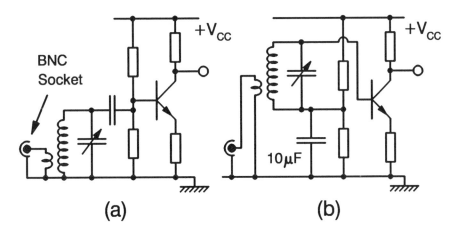

Figure 21.6: Two Radio-Frequency Amplifiers

Problem 20

Shown in Figure 21.7 is a tuned, resonant, radio-frequency amplifier. The load capacitance is known and fixed. A *ferrite bead* is a simple bead of ferrite and when it is threaded onto a wire that wire becomes a small inductor. They are much used in radio-frequency circuits. Given that the component values are as marked, what would be an appropriate value for the capacitor C?

What are the functions of the 1μF capacitors and the ferrite beads?

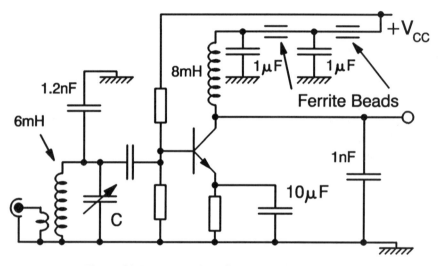

Figure 21.7: A Tuned Radio-Frequency Amplifier

Problem 21

Shown in Figure 21.8 is yet another radio-frequency amplifier. What are the functions of R_T, C_{T1}, C_{T2}, C_{in} and the diode?

Problem 22

In a simple radio variable capacitors are used as part of a tuned circuit to pick out the incoming frequency of interest. These capacitors are usually constructed from two interleaving sets of evenly spaced plates. One set is

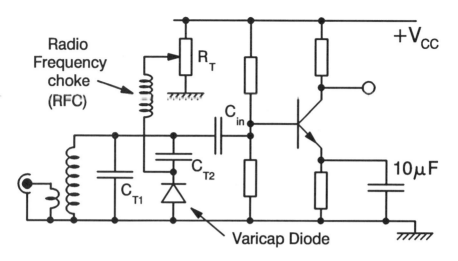

Figure 21.8: Another Radio-Frequency Tuned Amplifier

connected to ground and one set is connected to the "live" side of a parallel tuned circuit. (Usually the moving set is connected to ground - why?)

Two standard forms of variable capacitors are shown in Figure 21.9 Both can be sized to have the same maximum capacitance; only the shapes of the plates are different. Given that a variable capacitor is required for a radio, which type would you choose and why?

Problem 23

The circuit shown in Figure 21.10, with the exception of the resistor, R, purports to act as a variable form of a a single component which normally has a fixed value. What is that component and how does this circuit work? What is the value of V_{out} if the 10kΩ variable resistor is set to 5kΩ?

Problem 24

You are given a standard voltage/current multimeter, a 1.5V battery and any standard resistors and wire you might need. You are also given a totally unknown transistor, which may even be blown, and no information about it whatsoever. With the equipment available, what information can you obtain about the transistor and how would you go about finding it?

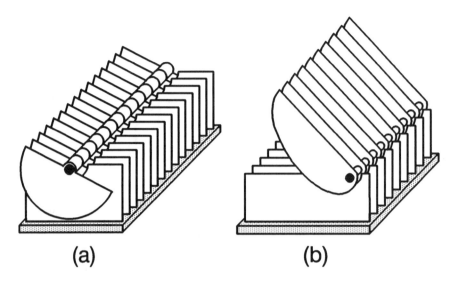

Figure 21.9: Two Variable Capacitors

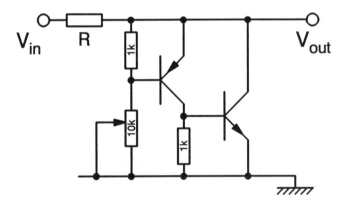

Figure 21.10: Transistor Circuit.

Problem 25

Consider the circuit shown in Figure 21.11. Sketch a graph of V_{out} against V_{in} for $-5V < V_{in} < 5V$. What is the function of this circuit?

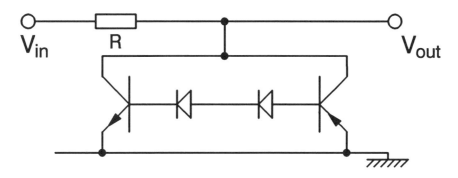

Figure 21.11: Transistor Circuit

Problem 26

Shown in Figure 21.12 are five *BAD* op-amp circuits. Work out why they are bad and then avoid them!

Problem 27

Electrolytic capacitors are polarised devices; that is voltage may be connected across them in only one direction. This disadvantage is normally outweighed by their very large capacitance per unit volume.

Shown in Figure 21.13 is a circuit containing electrolytic capacitors and diodes which can be used to replace a single circuit component. When is it used and why?

Problem 28

A logic question. Use common sense to answer it, not just the stuff from the course.

I have a water heater which turns ON if 250V AC (mains) is applied to it. I have two logic signals which, when ON, are 250V mains. When OFF then are open-circuit. They must NOT be connected together. The first logic signal indicates that the timer says it is time to heat the hot water. The second indicates that the user wants to heat the hot water. Design an *efficient* circuit which will provide the necessary signal to the heater.

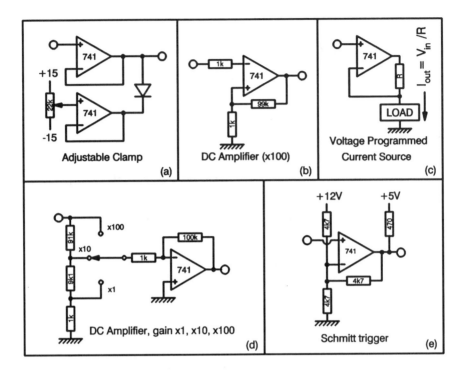

Figure 21.12: Bad Op-amp Circuits

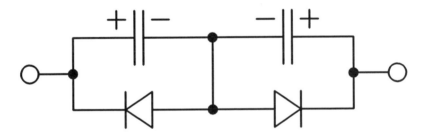

Figure 21.13: Capacitor/Diode Circuit

In my central heating system I have a motorised valve which controls the flow of water to the radiators. It is controlled by a 250V AC (mains) signal, mains ON implying valve OPEN. I want this valve open if the boiler is running (ie. if it has mains connected to it) AND the radiators are to be heated (ie. if it is winter). There is a switch which will supply 250V if I want the radiators on. Design an *efficient* circuit which will provide the necessary signal to the valve.

Problem 29

Shown in Figure 21.14 are four *BAD* op-amp circuits. Work out why they are bad and then avoid them!

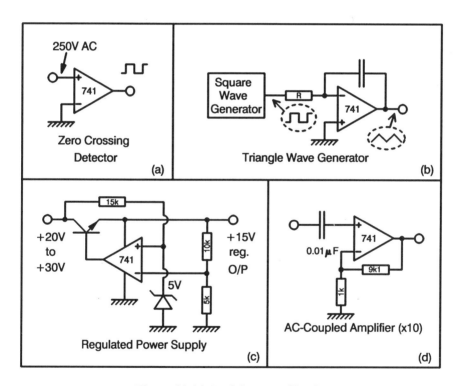

Figure 21.14: Bad Op-amp Circuits

Problem 30

We wish to drive an 8Ω load using class A amplifiers and NPN transistors *only*, with a low quiescent current. How?

Problem 31

This is a digital-type question using mains logic levels. Digital "1" is "mains connected" and digital "0" is "mains disconnected". Design mains-in/mains-out AND and OR gates.

Problem 32

How would you go about designing a very simple radio transmitter, such as a "bug".

Problem 33

Some power tools, such as electric saws, require special switches which cannot be left "ON". If the unit is left on and the power is disconnected somewhere other than at the switch, the switch must go "OFF" so that reconnecting the power will not result in the tool unexpectedly starting. Design an appropriate switch.

Problem 34

We have a solenoid which must be pulled in for long periods without getting too hot. It is basically a coil with a moderate inductance and an internal resistance of 10Ω. The available power supply is 10V and the static current in the solenoid required to keep it pulled in is to be about 0.5A. The power dissipation in the solenoid *together with its driving circuit* is to be less than 6W. Design the circuit.

Problem 35

Design a fluid level indicator which has *no moving parts*. (If the fluid is above a set level an indicator bulb is to light while if the fluid is below the set level the indicator is to go out.)

Problem 36

Design a circuit which will detect at what speed, and in which direction, a wheel is rotating *without touching it*. No extra moving parts are permitted.

Problem 37

A CMOS digital circuit outputs a ±7.5V digital signal. Design a circuit which will clip this to ±2.5V.

Problem 38

Design a tyre pressure indicator which will set off an alarm if the tyre pressure becomes lower than a set threshold *while driving*.

Problem 39

Sketch the output waveforms for the two circuits shown in Figures 21.15(a) and (b). They are not obvious.

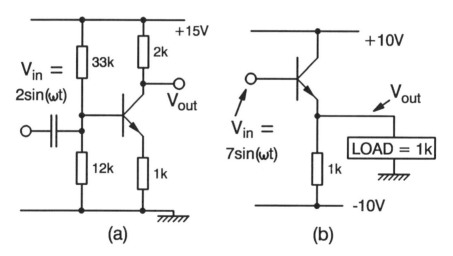

Figure 21.15: Two transistor circuits

Problem 40

A decent burglar alarm (to BS 4737) is a four wire system. Two wires are for the alarm and two are anti-tamper. If the two independent circuits are joined the alarm goes off. If one circuit is cut the alarm goes off. If the other is short-circuited the alarm goes off. Clearly, cutting the wire and then joining it again should not stop the alarm. However, there must be a reset switch. How might you design such a system?

Problem 41

A self-actuated bell module. This is part of the burglar alarm system referred to above. If the wire to the outside bell is cut it goes anyway, as does the siren inside the house. Design the circuit.

Problem 42

Design, in principle, a 2000V, 0.5A, regulated power supply.

Problem 43

Design a circuit which will measure capacitance in the range $0.01\mu F$ to $1\mu F$.

Problem 44

We have a clean room which is to run at an air pressure of slightly above normal atmospheric (to blow filth *out* the leaks). This pressure is maintained by filtered air being blown into the room through a number of vents. Thus the normal flow of air in the vents is inwards. If a single vent should fail it will effectively become a leak and air will flow through it outwards. Design a circuit which will detect the change in direction of the air flow. Because air will flow in a single direction for so long, any design which uses moving parts is sure to seize-up just when required so *no moving parts are permitted*.

Problem 45

Design a circuit which will set off an alarm if noise exceeds a set threshold.

Problem 46

We have a series of outputs, each of which is a current into ground. Design a circuit which will produce an output voltage proportional to their *sum*.

Problem 47

Consider the circuit shown in Figure 21.16(a). When V_B is a *fixed* bias voltage this circuit acts as a current source. That is, the current through the load is independent of the load's resistance. This is, of course, equivalent to saying that the current through the transistor is independent of its collector voltage.

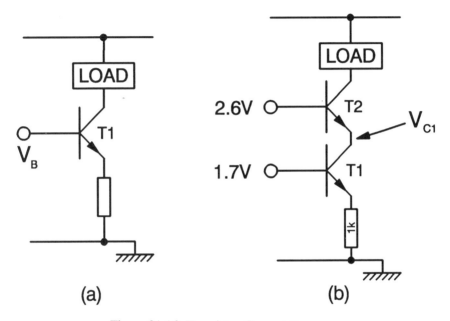

Figure 21.16: Transistor Current Sources.

Sketch a graph of I_C against V_C. Identify the region over which the transistor operates as a current source. Is the current actually constant? (Remember the Early effect.)

Now consider the modified circuit shown in Figure 21.16(b). This is a *cascode* circuit and transistor T2 is the cascode transistor. What is the value of V_{C1}? Comment on the effectiveness of this current source when compared to the previous one.

Problem 48

Shown in Figure 21.17 is a transistor biasing technique. T1 and T2 are matched. What is the value of V_{out}?

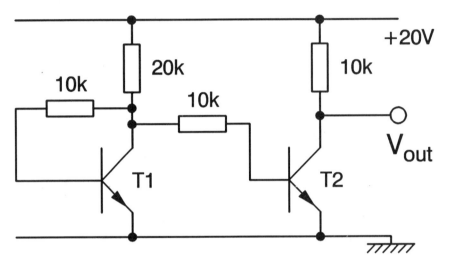

Figure 21.17: Transistor Biasing Technique

Why is this technique better than a simple resistor of appropriate value connected from T2 base to V_{dd}?

Problem 49

A particular type of Infra-Red (IR) sensor can be modelled by a current source, the value of which depends on the incident IR level. (This is only true, of course, if there is some bias voltage across it.) Should a British Standard Burglar (BSB) come into its field of view it draws a current of $\geq$ 1mA. If no burglar is present we can be sure it will draw less than 0.5mA.

Design a circuit which will cause a bell to ring (and keep ringing) should a BSB move into range. Burglar alarms use a standard +12V power supply. Include a reset switch.

Problem 50

The circuit shown in Figure 21.18(a) is a *Darlington pair*.

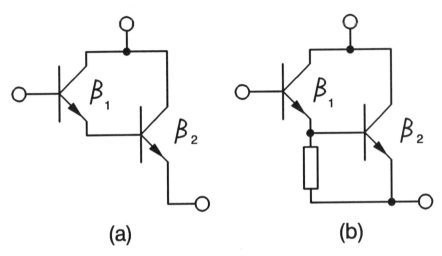

Figure 21.18: Darlington Pair

It can be considered to be a single high gain transistor. Find its β. It is frequently modified by the addition of a resistor as shown in Figure 21.18(b). Why is this?

Problem 51

By watching the average, cheap, electric toaster in operation we can note two significant points:-

1) The toaster makes a "clunck" noise *half-way* through its cycle

2) A second slice of toast, toasted immediately after a first, comes out the same as the first.

Bearing these two factors in mind, and remembering that despite all the manufacturers blurb the toaster contains just a timer and is not in the slightest interested in the actual colour of your toast, can you guess how the toaster works?

GENERAL COMPUTING BOOKS

Compiler Physiology for Beginners, M Farmer, 279pp, ISBN 0-86238-064-2
Concise Dictionary of Computing and Information Technology, D Lynch, 380 pages, ISBN 0-86238-268-8
File Structure and Design, M Cunningham, 211pp, ISBN 0-86238-065-0
Information Technology Dictionary of Acronyms and Abbreviations, D Lynch, 270pp, ISBN 0-86238-153-3
The IBM Personal Computer with BASIC and PC-DOS, B Kynning, 320pp, ISBN 0-86238-080-4
Project Skills Handbook, S Rogerson, 143pp, ISBN 0-86238-146-0

PROGRAMMING LANGUAGES

An Intro to LISP, P Smith, 130pp, ISBN 0-86238-187-8
An Intro to OCCAM 2 Programming: 2nd Ed, Bowler, *et al,* 109pp, ISBN 0-86238-227-0
C Simply, M Parr, 168pp, ISBN 0-86238-262-9
Cobol for Mainframe and Micro: 2nd Ed, D Watson, 177pp, ISBN 0-86238-211-4
Comparative Languages: 2nd Ed, J R Malone, 125pp, ISBN 0-86238-123-1
Fortran 77 for Non-Scientists, P Adman, 109pp, ISBN 0-86238-074-X
Fortran 77 Solutions to Non-Scientific Problems, P Adman, 150pp, ISBN 0-86238-087-1
Fortran Lectures at Oxford, F Pettit, 135pp, ISBN 0-86238-122-3
LISP: From Foundations to Applications, G Doukidis *et al,* 228pp, ISBN 0-86238-191-6
Programming for Change in Pascal, D Robson, 272pp, ISBN 0-86238-250-5
Prolog versus You, A Johansson, *et al,* 308pp, ISBN 0-86238-174-6
Simula Begin, G M Birtwistle, *et al,* 391pp, ISBN 0-86238-009-X
Structured Programming with COBOL & JSP: Vol 1, J B Thompson, 372pp, ISBN 0-86238-154-1, **Vol 2,** 354pp, ISBN 0-86238-245-9
The Intensive C Course: 2nd Edition, M Farmer, 186pp, ISBN 0-86238-190-8
The Intensive Pascal Course: 2nd Edition, M Farmer, 125pp, ISBN 0-86238-219-X

ASSEMBLY LANGUAGE PROGRAMMING

Coding the 68000, N Hellawell, 214pp, ISBN 0-86238-180-0
Computer Organisation and Assembly Language Programming, L Ohlsson & P Stenstrom, 128pp, ISBN 0-86238-129-0
What is machine code and what can you do with it? N Hellawell, 104pp, ISBN 0-86238-132-0

PROGRAMMING TECHNIQUES

Discrete-events simulations models in PASCAL/MT+ on a microcomputer, L P Jennergren, 135pp, ISBN 0-86238-053-7
Information and Coding, J A Llewellyn, 152pp, ISBN 0-86238-099-5
JSP - A Practical Method of Program Design, L Ingevaldsson, 204pp, ISBN 0-86238-107-X
Modular Software Design, M Stannett, 136pp, ISBN 0-86238-266-1

HARDWARE
Computers from First Principles, M Brown, 128pp, ISBN 0-86238-027-8
Fundamentals of Microprocessor Systems, P Witting, 525pp, ISBN 0-86238-030-8

ELECTRICAL & ELECTRONIC ENGINEERING
Analogue & Digital Signal Processing & Coding, P Grant, 450pp,
ISBN 0-86238-206-8
Analogue Circuit Design - a first course, H M Reekie, 250pp, ISBN 0-86238-286-6
Handbook of Electronics, J de Sousa Pires, approx 750pp, ISBN 0-86238-061-8
Electricity, T Johansson, 960pp, ISBN 0-86238-208-4
Interference-free Electronics, S Benda, ISBN 0-86238-255-6

NETWORKS
Communication Network Protocols: 3rd Ed, B Marsden, 561pp,
ISBN 0-86238-276-9
Computer Networks: Fundamentals and Practice, M D Bacon et al, 109pp,
ISBN 0-86238-028-6
Data Networks 1, Ericsson & Televerket, 250pp, ISBN 0-86238-193-2
Data Networks 2, Ericsson & Televerket, 159pp, ISBN 0-86238-221-1
Telecommunications: Telephone Networks 1, Ericsson & Televerket, 147pp,
ISBN 0-86238-093-6
Telecommunications: Telephone Networks 2, Ericsson & Televerket, 176pp,
ISBN 0-86238-113-4

GRAPHICS
An Introductory Course in Computer Graphics: 2nd Ed, R Kingslake, 163pp,
ISBN 0-86238-284-X
Techniques of Interactive Computer Graphics, A Boyd, 242pp, ISBN 0-86238-024-3
Two-dimensional Computer Graphics, S Laflin, 85pp, ISBN 0-86238-127-4

APPLICATIONS
Computers in Health and Fitness, J Abas, 106pp, ISBN 0-86238-155-X
Developing Expert Systems, G Doukidis, E Whitley, ISBN 0-86238-196-7
Expert Systems Introduced, D Daly, 180pp, ISBN 0-86238-185-1
Handbook of Finite Element Software, J Mackerle & B Fredriksson, approx
1000pp, ISBN 0-86238-135-5
Inside Data Processing: computers and their effective use in business: 2nd Ed,
A deWatteville, 150pp, ISBN 0-86238-252-1
Modelling with Spreadsheets, A Rothery, 200pp, ISBN 0-86238-258-0
Proceedings of the Third Scandinavian Conference on Image Analysis, P
Johansen & P Becker (eds) 426pp, ISBN 0-86238-039-1
Programmable Control Systems, G Johannesson, 136pp, ISBN 0-86238-046-4
Risk and Reliability Appraisal on Microcomputers, G Singh, with G Kiangi,
142pp, ISBN 0-86238-159-2
Statistics with Lotus 1-2-3: 2nd Ed, M Lee & J Soper, 207pp, ISBN 0-86238-244-0

Linear Programming: A Computational Approach: 2nd Ed, K K Lau, 150pp,
ISBN 0-86238-182-7
Programming for Beginners: the structured way, D Bell & P Scott, 178pp,
ISBN 0-86238-130-4
Software Engineering for Students, M Coleman & S Pratt, 195pp,
ISBN 0-86238-115-0
Software Taming with Dimensional Design, M Coleman & S Pratt, 164pp,
ISBN 0-86238-142-8

MATHEMATICS AND COMPUTING

Fourier Transforms in Action, F Pettit, 133pp, ISBN 0-86238-088-X
Generalised Coordinates, L G Chambers, 90pp, ISBN 0-86238-079-0
Statistics and Operations Research, I P Schagen, 300pp, ISBN 0-86238-077-4
Teaching of Modern Engineering Mathematics, L Rade (ed), 225pp,
ISBN 0-86238-173-8
Teaching of Statistics in the Computer Age, L Rade (ed), 248pp, ISBN 0-86238-090-1
The Essentials of Numerical Computation, M Bartholomew-Biggs, 241pp,
ISBN 0-86238-029-4

DATABASES AND MODELLING

Computer Systems Modelling & Development, D Cornwell, 291pp,
ISBN 0-86238-220-3
An Introduction to Data Structures, B Boffey, D Yates, 250pp, ISBN 0-86238-076-6
Database Analysis and Design: 2nd Ed, H Robinson, 378pp, ISBN 0-86238-018-9
Databases and Database Systems: 2nd Ed, E Oxborrow, 256pp, ISBN 0-86238-091-X
Data Bases and Data Models, B Sundgren, 134pp, ISBN 0-86238-031-6
Text Retrieval and Document Databases, J Ashford & P Willett, 125pp,
ISBN 0-86238-204-1
Information Modelling, J Bubenko (ed), 687pp, ISBN 0-86238-006-5

UNIX

An Intro to the Unix Operating System, C Duffy, 152pp, ISBN 0-86238-143-6
Operating Systems through Unix, G Emery, 96pp, ISBN 0-86238-086-3

SYSTEMS ANALYSIS & SYSTEMS DESIGN

Systems Analysis and Development: 3rd Ed, P Layzell & P Loucopoulos, 284pp,
ISBN 0-86238-215-7
SSADM Techniques, Lejk, et al, 350pp, ISBN 0-86238-224-6
Computer Systems: Where Hardware meets Software, C Machin, 200pp,
ISBN 0-86238-075-8
Microcomputer Systems: hardware and software, J Tierney, 168pp,
ISBN 0-86238-218-1
Distributed Applications and Online Dialogues: a design method for application
systems, A Rasmussen, 271pp, ISBN 0-86238-105-3